CHORALE COLLECTION

EASTMAN SCHOOL OF MUSIC PUBLICATIONS

No. 1   Ruth Zimmerman Steese

CHORAL MUSIC IN THE AMERICAN COLLEGES

No. 2   Leonard Ellinwood

MUSICA HERMANNI CONTRACTI

No. 3   Gustave Fredric Soderlund

EXAMPLES ILLUSTRATING THE DEVELOPMENT OF MELODIC LINE
AND CONTRAPUNTAL STYLE FROM GREEK MELODY TO MOZART

For use in classes of Counterpoint and History of Music

No. 4   Gustave Fredric Soderlund

EXAMPLES OF GREGORIAN CHANT AND WORKS BY ORLANDUS LASSUS,
GIOVANNI PIERLUIGI PALESTRINA, AND MARC ANTONIO INGEGNERI

For use in classes of Counterpoint

No. 5   Harold Gleason

METHOD OF ORGAN PLAYING

No. 6   Nelson Watson

A MODERN METHOD FOR THE DOUBLE BASS

No. 7   Thomas Austin-Ball

ANSWERS TO SOME VOCAL QUESTIONS

No. 8   Karl Van Hoesen

HANDBOOK OF CONDUCTING

No. 9   Elvera Wonderlich

CHORALE COLLECTION

Including 156 Chorales by J. S. Bach, 22 Swedish Chorales,
and 20 Norwegian Chorales.

EASTMAN SCHOOL OF MUSIC PUBLICATION No. 9

CHORALE COLLECTION

including

156 Chorales by J. S. Bach, 22 Swedish Chorales, and 20 Norwegian Chorales

Selected and Edited by

ELVERA WONDERLICH

of the

Theory Department of the Eastman School of Music of the University of Rochester

Published by the Eastman School of Music
of the University of Rochester, Rochester, New York

1943

Published by F. S. CROFTS & CO., INC.
101 FIFTH AVENUE, NEW YORK 3, N. Y.

Lithoprinted in U.S.A.

EDWARDS BROTHERS, INC.

ANN ARBOR, MICHIGAN

1943

FOREWORD

The Eastman School of Music is happy to present this
publication of chorales as edited by Elvera Wonderlich of the
theory department of the Eastman School of Music. This volume
will prove especially valuable to the student of the technique
of part-writing conceived in the period of composition in which
clearly defined tonalities were dominant.   There is no type of
music better suited to give him technical guidance and example.

In this edition Miss Wonderlich has carefully selected
and ably edited 156 Bach chorales in a manner which makes them
of great practical value to the young student. The book is especially notable, however, for the inclusion of 42 Swedish and
Norwegian chorales of unusual beauty.   In addition to their
esthetic value, these Scandinavian chorales in the stark sim-
plicity of their harmonization form a valuable contrast to the
more familiar chorales of Bach.

In this work of selecting and editing the chorales of
Bach, as well as in the perhaps more difficult task of present-
ing outstanding examples from the field of Scandinavian chorales,
Miss Wonderlich has shown evidence of the high quality of her
scholarship and has contributed a volume which should be of dis-
tinct aid to every student of the art of part-writing.

Howard Hanson

Director Eastman School of Music

This collection of chorales is intended primarily for use in the theory classes of the Eastman School of Music. The German title of each of the chorales by Bach is usually the first line of the hymn which was most commonly associated with the chorale melody. In instances where there seems to be little or no relation between title and text, the confusion may be due to the fact that Bach has selected some stanza other than the first for that particular harmonization.

The texts for the Bach chorales have been taken from the larger works in which they occur, including the St. Matthew Passion, the St. John Passion, the Christmas Oratorio, the motet, Jesu meine Freude, and various cantatas. Those chorales, for which the words have been lost, have as texts the first stanza of the hymn of that name. Great care has been taken to provide all of the chorales with translations which are as close to the original as possible, with, it is to be hoped, some literary value.

The confusion between the vocal bass and the basso continuo, which exists in many earlier editions of Bach chorales, is avoided in this publication by giving the vocal bass only. Reference to the volume and page in the Bachgesellschaft Edition of the complete works of Bach is given with each chorale, also the name of the larger work from which the chorale is taken, the source of the hymn and the melody, and the name of the translator.

Forty-two Scandinavian chorales have been included in this collection to afford students an opportunity of becoming acquainted with Swedish and Norwegian harmonizations. The Swedish chorales are taken from Koral-Bok och Svenska messan med körer för sopran-, alt-, tenor-och bas-röster, with translations from The Hymnal and Order of Service. The Norwegian chorales are from Koralbok for den Norske Kirke, with translations from The Lutheran Hymnary. The numbers in parentheses following the Scandinavian titles refer to Koral-Bok och Svenska messan and Koralbok for den Norske Kirke.

The editor is greatly indebted to Mr. Allen I. McHose and Miss Ruth North-Northup of the Eastman School of Music for assistance in selecting the chorales; to the Rev. Felix Hanson, Dr. C. W. Fox, and Mr. William Kimmel for translations made especially for this publication; to Miss Beatrix Lien, Miss Myrtle Jensen, and Professor Per Olsson for help in finding translations for the Scandinavian chorales; and to the following publishers for permission to use texts and music:

Carl Fischer, Inc., New York, as agents of the Oxford University Press, London, for translations by C. S. Terry of Numbers 8, 17, 25, 39, 49, 52, 54, 63, 81, 88, 95, 96, 98, 100, 106, 121, 131, 132, taken from The Four-Part Chorals of J. S. Bach, edited by C. S. Terry.

G. Schirmer, Inc., New York, for translations by Charles N. Boyd and Albert Riemenschneider of Numbers 45, 66, 87, and 130, taken from Chorales by Johann Sebastian Bach, Book I, selected and edited by Charles N. Boyd and Albert Riemenschneider.

Hall & McCreary Company, Chicago, for a translation by August Crill of Number 102 taken from the Anniversary Collection of Bach Chorales by Walter E. Buszin.

The H. W. Gray Co., American agents for Novello & Co., Ltd., London, for translations by Miss H. F. H. Johnston of Numbers 71, 72, 73, and 75, taken from The Passion of Our Lord According to St. Matthew by J. S. Bach; for translations by Dr. T. A. Lacey of Numbers 21, 89, and 90, taken from The Passion of Our Lord According to St. John by J. S. Bach; for translations by J. Troutbeck of Numbers 69, 79, 126, 134, and 136, taken from The Passion of Our Lord According to St. John by J. S. Bach; for a translation by J. Troutbeck of Number 125 from The Passion of Our Lord According to St. Matthew by J. S. Bach; and for the translations by Paul England of Numbers 15 and 16, taken from the cantata Christ Lay in Death's Dark Prison by J. S. Bach.

Oliver Ditson Co., Philadelphia, for translations by John S. Dwight of Numbers 74, 76, 78, 86, 144, 145, and 152, taken from The Passion According to St. Matthew by J. S. Bach as revised and edited by Louis Koemmenich.

H. Aschehoug and Co., Oslo, Norway, for the music of the Norwegian chorales, taken from Koralbok for den Norske Kirke.

Augustana Book Concern, Rock Island, Illinois, for the music of the Swedish chorales taken from Koral-Bok och Svenska messan med körer för sopran-, alt-, tenor-och basröster; and for the translations of the Swedish chorales taken from The Hymnal and Order of Service.

Augsburg Publishing House, Minneapolis, Minnesota, for translations of the Norwegian chorales and also Numbers 6, 7, 10, and 15 of the Swedish chorales taken from The Lutheran Hymnary.

ELVERA WONDERLICH

CONTENTS

CHORALES by Johann Sebastian Bach

Page

Befiehl du deine Wege   )
O Haupt voll Blut und Wunden)   see   Herzlich thut mich verlangen
)
Gott sei uns gnädig und barmherzig,   see   Meine Seele erhebt den Herren

In allen meinen Taten   )
Nun ruhen alle Wälder   )   see   O Welt, ich muss dich lassen
O Welt, sieh hier dein Leben)

Nun lieget alles unter dir,   see   Ermuntre dich, mein schwacher Geist

Wach' auf, mein Herz,   see   Nun lasst uns Gott, dem Herren

Wär' Gott nicht mit uns diese Zeit,   see   Wo Gott der Herr nicht bei uns hält

Weg, mein Herz, mit den Gedanken,   see   Freu' dich sehr, o meine Seele

SWEDISH CHORALES

NORWEGIAN CHORALES

BIBLIOGRAPHY

Bach-Gesellschaft, J. S. BACHS WERKE, Leipzig: Bach-Gesellschaft, 1851-1899.

Frances E. Cox, HYMNS FROM THE GERMAN, second edition, London: Rivingtons, 1864.

D. Albert Fischer, DAS DEUTSCHE EVANGELISCHE KIRCHENLIED, six volumes, Gütersloh: C. Bertelsmann, 1904-1916.

THE HYMNAL AND ORDER OF SERVICE, Rock Island: Augustana Book Concern, 1927.

John Julian, A DICTIONARY OF HYMNOLOGY, London: John Murry, 1908.

KORALBOK FOR DEN NORSKE KIRKE, Oslo: H. Aschehoug & Co., 1936.

KORAL BOK OCH SVENSKA MESSAN MED KÖRER FÖR SOPRAN-, ALT-, TENOR-, OCH BASRÖSTER. Rock Island: Augustana Book Concern, 1892.

James Franklin Lambert, LUTHER'S HYMNS, Philadelphia: General Council Publication House, 1917.

THE LUTHERAN HYMNARY, Minneapolis: Augsburg Publishing House, 1923.

Richard Massie, LUTHER'S SPIRITUAL SONGS, London: Hatchard & Co., 1854.

Arthur Tozer Russell, PSALMS AND HYMNS, Cambridge: Deighton, 1851.

Ludwig Schoeberlein, SCHATZ DES LITURGISCHEN CHOR-UND GEMEINDEGESANGS, three volumes, Göttingen: Vandenhoeck und Ruprecht, 1865-1872.

Charles Sanford Terry, THE FOUR-PART CHORALS OF J. S. BACH, London and New York: Oxford University Press, 1929.

Philipp Wackernagel, DAS DEUTSCHE KIRCHENLIED, five volumes, Leipzig: B. G. Teubner, 1864-1877.

Catherine Winkworth, CHORALE BOOK FOR ENGLAND, London: Longman, Green, Longman, Roberts, and Green, 1863.

------------LYRA GERMANICA, First and Second Series, London: Longman & Co., 1855-1858.

Johannes Zahn, DIE MELODIEN DER DEUTSCHEN EVANGELISCHEN KIRCHENLIEDER, six volumes Gütersloh: C. Bertelsmann, 1889-1893.

CHORALES
By J. S. Bach
1-156

No. 1.   ACH GOTT UND HERR, WIE GROSS UND SCHWER
(B.W. XXXIX p. 178)

Hymn by Johann Major 1613
Translation by Catherine Winkworth

Melody from As hymnodus sacer, Leipzig, 1625

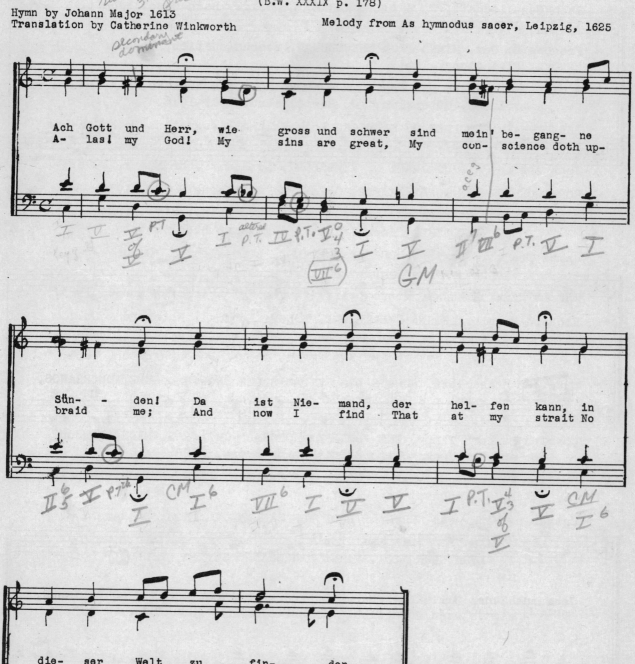

Ach Gott und Herr, wie gross und schwer sind mein' be- gang- ne
A- las! my God! My sins are great, My con- science doth up-

Sün- den! Da ist Nie- mand, der hel- fen kann, in
braid me; And now I find That at my strait No

die- ser Welt zu fin- den.
man hath power to aid me.

Cantata 48 Ich elender Mensch (B.W. X p. 288)

Hymn by Johann Major 1613   Melody from As hymnodus sacer, Leipzig,1625
Translation by Catherine Winkworth

Soll's ja so   sein,   dass   Straf' und Pein auf Sün- den   fol- gen
If   pain and woe   Must   fol- low sin, Then   be   my   path still

müs-   sen: so   fahr' hier fort und   schone   dort, und
rough-   er.   Here spare me   not; If   heaven I win, On

lass mich hier wohl bü - - - - - - - - - - - ssen.
earth I   glad- ly suf - - - - - - - - - - - fer.

2

No. 3   ACH GOTT, VOM HIMMEL SIEH DAREIN

Cantata 153 Schau, lieber Gott, wie meine Feind.(B.W. XXXII p. 43)

Hymn attributed to David Denicke 1646   Melody from Erfurter Enchiridion 1524
Translation Cento

Schau', lie- ber Gott, wie mei- ne Feind'; da- mit ich stets muss
so li- stig und so mach- tig seind', dass sie mich leichtlich
Be- hold, O Lord, the many foes, With whom I struggle
'Gainst many and such mighty woes, My strenth a- vai- leth

käm- pfen, Herr, wo mich dei- ne Gnad' nicht hält, so
däm- pfen! Lord, with Thy grace my soul re- fresh! Then
ev- ney- er:

kann der Teu- fel, Fleisch und Welt mich leicht in Un- glück
shall the De- vil, World, and Flesh No more pre- vail a-

stür- zen.
gainst me.

3

ACH GOTT, VOM HIMMEL SIEH' DAREIN
Cantata 2 Ach Gott, vom Himmel sieh' darein (B.W. I p. 72)'

Hymn by Martin Luther 1524
Translation by Frances E. Cox

Melody from Erfurter Enchiridion 1524

Dass wollst du Gott be- wah- ren rein für diesem arg'n Ge-
Und lass uns dir be- foh- len sein, dass sich's in uns nicht
Thy truth thou wilt pre- serve, O Lord, From this vile gen- e-
Make us to lean up- on thy Word, With calm an- ti- ci-

schlech- te, der gott- los' Hauf' sich um- her find't, wo
flech- te,
ra- tion; The wicked walk on every side When,

sol- che lo- se Leute sind in deinem Volk er-
'mid thy flock, the vile a- bide In power and ex- al-

ha- - - - - - - ben.
ta- - - - - - - tion.

Cantata 3 Ach Gott wie manches Herzeleid (B.W. I p. 94)

Hymn attributed to Martin Moller 1587   Melody from As hymnodus sacer 1587
Translation by J.C. Jacobi

Er- halt' mein Herz im Glau- ben rein, so leb' und sterb' ich
Pre- serve my faith from er- ror free, That I may live and

dir al- lein. Je- su, mein Trost, hör' mein Be- gier': o
die in Thee. Lord Je- sus Christ, hear my de- sire, To

mein Hei- land, wär ich bei dir!
praise Thee in the heavenly choir.

No. 6   ACH GOTT WIE MANCHES HERZELEID

Cantata 153 Schau lieber Gott (B.W. XXXII p. 58)

Hymn attributed to Martin Moller 1587   Melody from As hymnodus sacer 1625
Translation by J.C. Jacobi

Drum will ich, weil ich le- be noch,
So then, as long as life shall be,

das Kreuz dir fröh- lich tra- gen nach;
I'll bear the Cross and fol- low Thee:

mein Gott mach' mich dar- zu be- reit,
O, Lord, pre- pare this heart of mine,

es dient zum Be- sten al- le- zeit.
Let it to no- thing else in- cline.

6

(B.W. XXXIX p. 179)

Hymn by Joh. Flitner 1661   Melody from Joh. Flitner's 'Suscitabulum musicum' 1661
Translation by Catherine Winkworth

Ach, was soll ich Sün- der mach- en? ach, was soll ich
What shall I, a sin- ner do Lord? Whither shall I

fan- gen an,   mein Ge- wis- sen klagt mich an,
turn for aid?   Sins that make me sore a- fraid

es be- gin- net auf- zu- wachen; dies ist mei- ne
Con- science wak- ing brings to view, Lord. This my con- fi-

Zu- ver- sicht,   meinen Je- sum lass' ich nicht.
d'ence shall be,   Je- sus, I will cleave to Thee.

Cantata 112 Der Herr ist mein getreuer Hirt (B.W. XXIV p. 48)

Hymn adapted by Decius 1525
Translation by C. S. Terry   Melody from Schumann's Geistliche Lieder 1539

Gu- tes und die Barm- her- zig- keit fol- gen mir nach im
und ich werd' blei- ben al- le- zeit im Haus des Her- ren
And so, throughout my length of days His goodness faileth
And fain am I to sing His praise With- in His courts for-

Le- ben auf Erd' in christ- li- cher Gemein', und
e- nev- er, His church doth us on earth sustain, And
ev- er.

nach dem Tod da werd' ich sein bei Chri- sto, mei- nem
af- ter death in heaven we'll reign, From Je- sus part- ed

Her- - ren.
nev- - er.

No. 9 ALLEIN ZU DIR HERR JESU CHRIST

Cantata 33 Allein zu dir, Herr Jesu Christ (B.W. Vll p. 114)

Hymn: Johann Schneesing 1542
Translation by Catherine Winkworth

Melody from Babst's Geystliche Lieder 1545

Ehr' sei Gott in dem höch- sten Thron, dem
und Je- sum Christ, sein'm lieb- sten Sohn, der
Glo- ry to God in high- est Heaven. The
To His dear Son, for sin- ners giv'n, Whose

Va- ter al- zeit - - - - - - ler Gü- te. und
uns all- zeit - - - - - be- hü- te. To.
Fa- ther of grace e- - - - ter- nal love; To
watch- ful grace we - - - - dai- ly prove;

Gott, dem hei- li- gen Gei- ste, der uns sein' Hülf' all-
God the Ho- ly Ghost on high; Oh, ev- er be His

9

zeit lei- ste, da- mit wir ihm ge- fäl- lig sein, hier
com- fort nigh; And teach us, free from sin and fear, To

in die- - ser Zeit und fol- gends in der E-
please- - Him here, And serve Him in the sin- -

- wig- keit.
- less sphere.

10

Hymn by Johann Heermann 1636
Translation by Elvera Wonderlich

Melody by Johann Crüger 1649

Als Je- sus Christus in der Nacht, da- rin er ward ver-
That night when Je- sus Christ, our Lord By His dis- ci- ple

ra- then, auf un- ser Heil war ganz be- dacht, das-
was be-tray'd, To us on earth He gave His Word That

selb' uns zu er- stat- ten.
ex- pi- a- tion would be made.

11

No. 11   AUF MEINEN LIEBEN GOTT
Cantata 5 Wo soll ich fliehen hin (B.W. I p. 150)

Hymn by Johann Heerman 1630   Melody by Johann Schein 1627
Translation anonymous

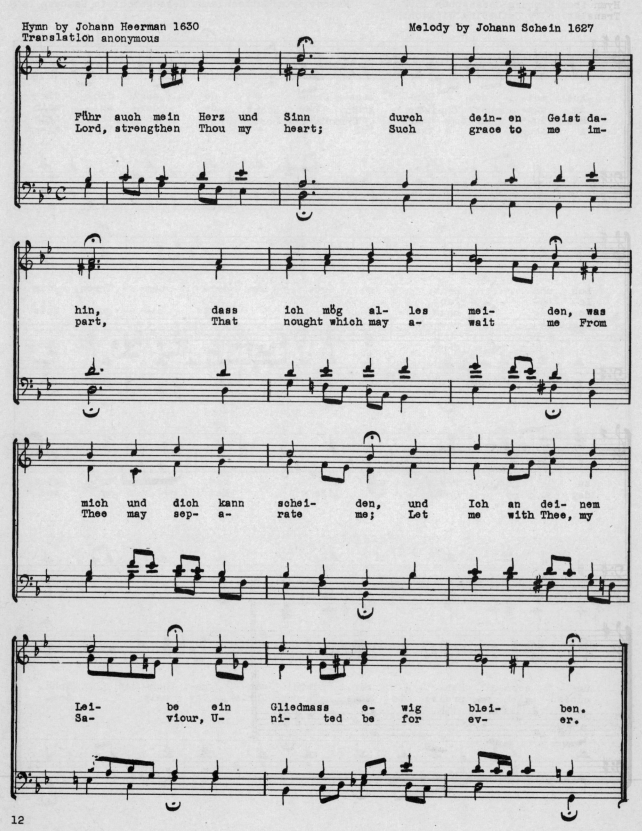

Führ auch mein Herz und Sinn   durch dein-en Geist da-
Lord, strengthen Thou my heart; Such grace to me im-

hin,   dass ich mög al- les mei- den, was
part,   That nought which may a- wait me From

mich und dich kann schei- den, und Ich an dei- nem
Thee may sep-a- rate me; Let me with Thee, my

Lei-   be ein Gliedmass e- wig blei- ben.
Sa-   viour, U- ni- ted be for ev- er.

12

No. 12 AUS MEINES HERZENS GRUNDE
(B.W. XXXIX p. 184)

Hymn from Hamburg Gesangbuch 1592
Translation by Catherine Winkworth

Melody from Cathechismus Gesangbüchlein, Hamburg, 1598

Aus mei- nes Her- zens Grun- - de sag' ich dir
in die- ser Mor- gen- stun- - de dar- zu mein
My in- most heart now rais- - es, In this fair
A song of thank- ful prais- - es To Thine al-

Lob und Dank, o Gott in dei- nem Thron, dir
Le- be- lang, And as I have be- gun This
morn- ing hour, And as I have be- gun This
might- y power; And as I have be- gun This

zu Lob, Preis und Eh- - ren, durch Chri- stum,
day, my God, my life be Be- gun and
day, my God, my life be Be- gun and

un- sern Her- - ren, dein' ein- ge- bor- nen Sohn.
closed with praise to Thee Through Christ, Thy only Son.

13

No. 13 AUS TIEFER NOT SCHREI' ICH ZU DIR
Cantata 38, Aus tiefer Noth schrei ich zu dir. (B.W. VII p. 300)

Hymn by Martin Luther 1524
Translation by Catherine Winkworth

Melody from Walter's Geystliche Gesangk Buchleyn 1524

Ob   bei uns ist der Sün- den viel, bei Gott ist viel mehr
sein' Hand zu hel-fen hat kein Ziel, wie gross auch sei der
Though great our sins and sore our woes, His grace much more a-
His   help-ing love no lim-it knows, Our ut- most need it

Gna- - de,   Er   ist al- lein der gu- te
Scha- - de.   Our   kind and faith- ful Shep- herd,
bound- - eth;
sound- - eth:

Hirt, der I- sra- el er- lö- sen wird
He,   Who shall at last set Israel free

aus   sei- nem Sün- den al- - len.
From all their sin and sor- - row.

14

No. 14   BEFIEHL DU DEINE WEGE
(B.W. XXXIX p. 186)

Hymn by Paul Gerhardt 1656   Melody from Gesius' Enchiridion 1603
Translation by Frances E. Cox

15

No. 15 CHRIST LAG IN TODESBANDEN

Cantata No. 4 Christ lag in Todesbanden (B.W. I P. 124)

Hymn by Martin Luther 1524
Translation by Paul England

Melody from Walter's Geystliche Gesangk Buchleyn 1524

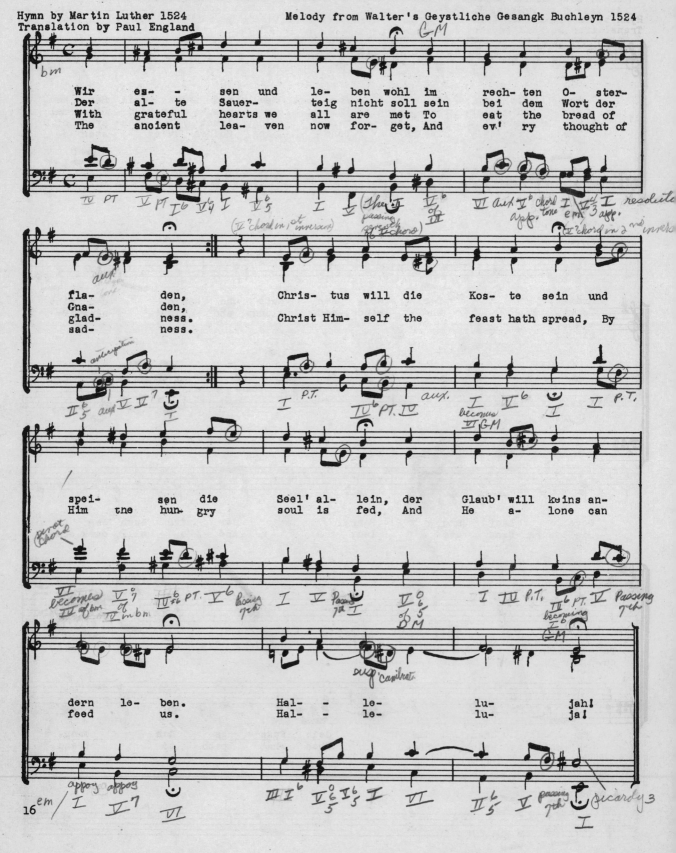

Cantata 158 Der Friede sei mit dir (B.W. XXXII 154)

Hymn by Martin Luther 1524
Translation by Paul England

Melody from Walther's Geystliche Gesangk Buchleyn 1524

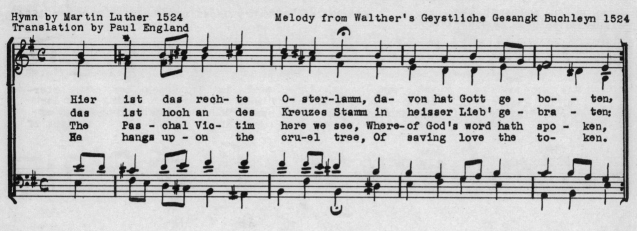

Hier ist das rech-te O-ster-lamm, da-von hat Gott ge - bo - ten,
das ist hoch an des Kreuzes Stamm in heisser Lieb' ge - bra - ten:
The Pas - chal Vic-tim here we see, Where-of God's word hath spo - ken,
Ha hangs up - on the cru-el tree, Of saving love the to - ken.

dess Blut zeichnet uns're Thür', dass hält der Glaub' dem
His blood ran - soms us from sin, And Death no more can

To- de für, der Wür- ger kann uns nicht rüh - ren. Hal - le - lu - ja!
ter in. Now Satan can- not harm - us, Hal- le - lu - jah!

* A natural in the Bachgesellschaft Edition

No. 17   CHRIST UNSER HERR, ZUM JORDAN KAM

Cantata 176 Es ist ein trotzig und verzagt Ding. (B.W. XXXV p. 198)

Hymn by Paul Gerhardt 1656   Melody from Walter's Geystliche Gesangk Buchleyn 1524
Translation by C. Sanford Terry

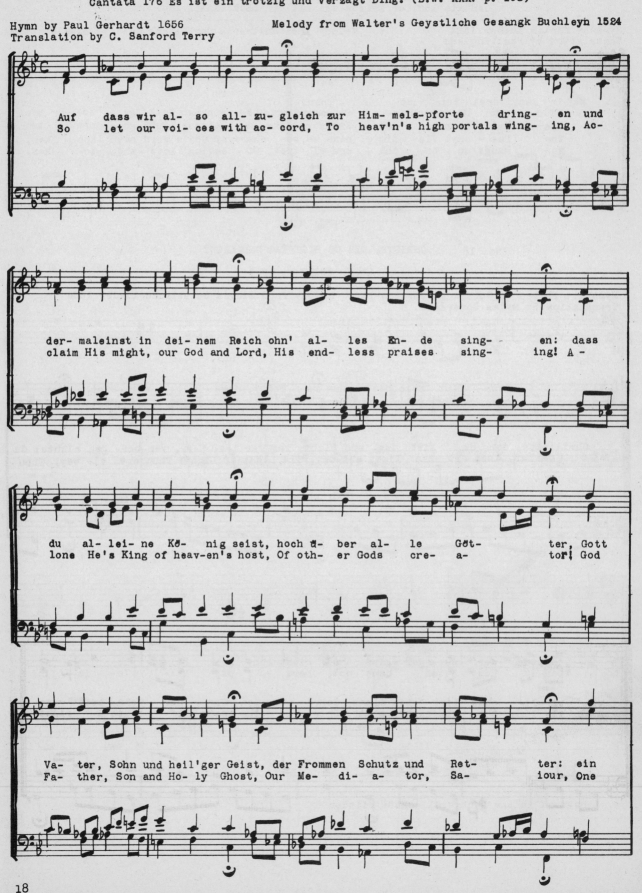

Auf   dass wir al- so all- zu- gleich zur Him- mels- pforte   dring-   en und
So   let our voi- ces with ac- cord, To heav'n's high portals wing- ing, Ac-

der- maleinst in dei- nem Reich ohn' al- les En- de sing-- en: dass
claim His might, our God and Lord, His end- less praises sing- ing! A-

du al- lei- ne Kö- nig seist, hoch ü- ber al- le Göt- ter, Gott
lone He's King of heav-en's host, Of oth- er Gods cre- a- tor! God

Va- ter, Sohn und heil'ger Geist, der Frommen Schutz und Ret- ter: ein
Fa- ther, Son and Ho- ly Ghost, Our Me- di- a- tor, Sa- iour, One

We- sen, drei Per- so- nen.
God- head in Three Per- sons!

No. 18   CHRISTE, DER DU BIST TAG UND LICHT

(B.W. XXXIX p. 187)

Hymn attributed to Wolfgang Meusslin 1526 Melody from Klug's Geistliche Lieder 1535
Translation by Myles Coverdale

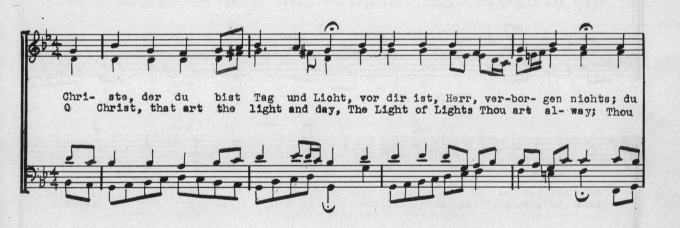

Chri- ste, der du bist Tag und Licht, vor dir ist, Herr, ver-bor- gen nichts; du
O   Christ, that art the light and day, The Light of Lights Thou art al- way; Thou

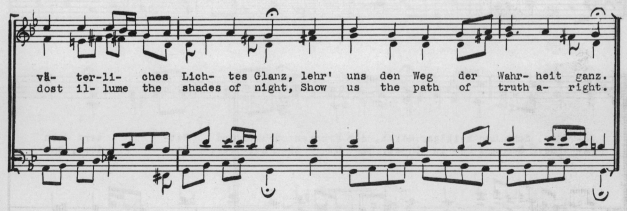

vä- ter-li- ches Lich- tes Glanz, lehr' uns den Weg der Wahr-heit ganz.
dost il- lume the shades of night, Show us the path of truth a- right.

No. 19   CHRISTE, DU BEISTAND DEINER KREUZGEMEINE
(B.W. XXXIX p. 187)

Hymn by Apelles von Löwenstern 1644   Melody by Appelles von Löwenstern 1644
Translation by Catherine Winkworth

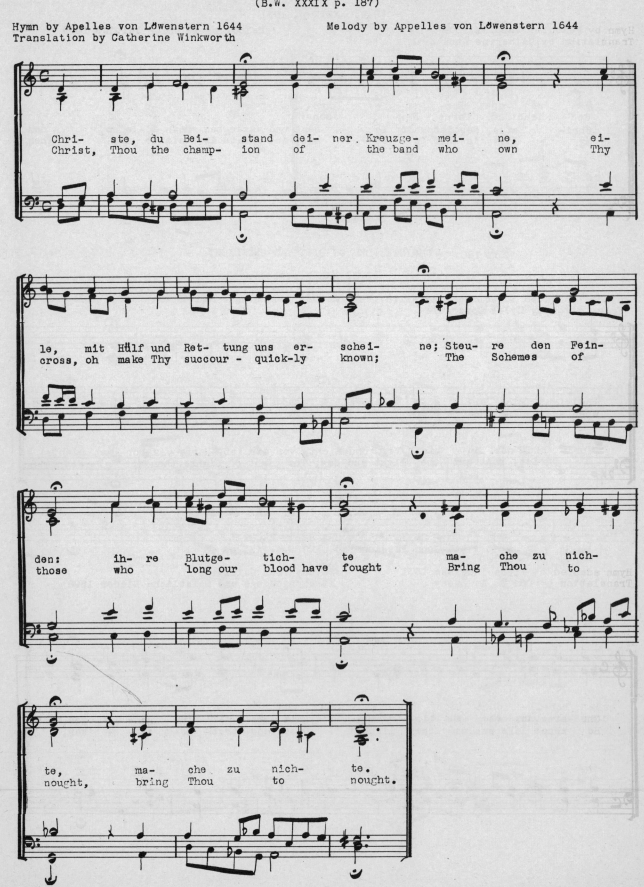

Chri- ste, du Bei- stand dei- ner Kreuzge- mei- ne, ei-
Christ, Thou the champ- ion of the band who own Thy

le, mit Hülf und Ret- tung uns er- schei- ne; Steu- re den Fein-
cross, oh make Thy succour quick-ly known; The Schemes of

den: ih- re Blutge- tich- te ma- che zu nich-
those who long our blood have fought Bring Thou to

te, ma- che zu nich- te.
nought, bring Thou to nought.

20

No. 20   CHRISTUS DER IST MEIN LEBEN
(B.W. XXXIX p. 191)

Hymn by Melchior Vulpius 1609   Melody by Melchior Vulpius 1609
Translation by Catherine Winkworth

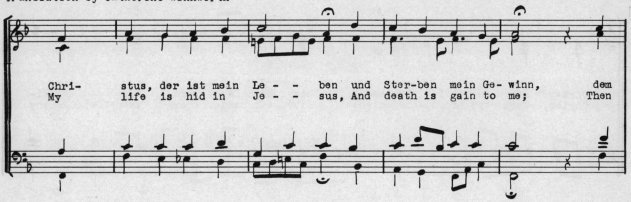

Chri-   stus, der ist mein Le - - ben und Ster-ben mein Ge- winn,   dem
My   life is hid in Je - - sus, And death is gain to me;   Then

thu' ich   mich er-   ge- ben, mit Freud' fahr' ich da-   hin.
when so-   e'er He   plea-ses, I   meet   it   will-ing-   ly.

No. 21   CHRISTUS DER UNS SELIG MACHT
St. John Passion (No. 12) B.W. XII p. 43

Hymn adapted by Michael Weisse 1531   Melody from Calvisius'
Translation by Dr. T. A. Lacey   Kirchengesenge und Geistliche Lieder 1598

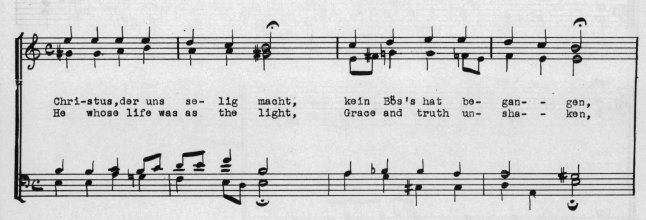

Chri-stus,der uns   se- lig macht,   kein Bös's hat be-   gan- - gen,
He   whose life was as   the light,   Grace and truth un- sha- - ken,

21

der ward für uns in der Nacht als ein Dieb ge- fan- gen
In the dark-ness of the night Like a thief was ta- - ken;

ge- führt vor gott- lo- se Leut' und fälschlich ver- kla- - get,
Judg- ment of a god- less court, Wit- ness falsely of- - fered,

ver- lacht, ver- höhnt und ver- speit, wie denn die Schrift sa- - get.
Scorn and spitting, ri- bald sport, As foretold, He suf- fered.

22

No. 22   CHRISTUS IST ERSTANDEN, HAT ÜBERWUNDEN

(B.W. XXXIX p. 192)

Hymn by Michael Weisse 1531   Melody from Speer's Choral Gesang Buch 1692
Translation by William Kimmel

Chri-stus ist er-stan-den, hat ü-ber-wun-den; Gnad' ist
Christ our Lord is ris-en, Now death hath He bound; Van-quished

nun vor-han-den, Wahr-heit wird fun-den. Da-rum, lie-ben
is the pris-on, And God's truth is found. Therefore Christians

Leu-te, freut euch heu-te, lo-bet eu-ren Her-
now re-joice, And with glad-some voice. Cease your singing nev-

ren, Je-sum, den Kö-nig der Eh-ren.
er, Praise to Christ the King for-ev-er.

23

(B.W. XXXIX p. 193)

Hymn by Johann Horn 1544   Tenor melody by Ludwig Senfl 1534
Translation by Elvera Wonderlich

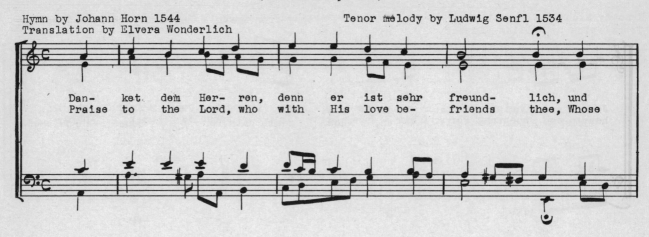

Dan-   ket dem Her- ren, denn er ist sehr freund-   lich, und
Praise   to   the Lord, who with His love be- friends   thee, Whose

sei- ne Güt' und Wahr- heit blei- bet e- wig-   lich.
truth and kind- ness will en- dure e- ter- nal-   ly.

No. 24   DAS ALTE JAHR VERGANGEN IST

(B.W. XXXIX p. 194)

Hymn attributed to Johannes Steuerlein 1588
Translation by J. C. Jacobi   Melody attributed to Johannes Steuerlein 1588

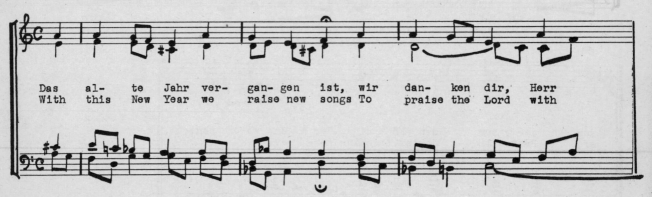

Das   al-   te Jahr ver- gan- gen ist, wir   dan- ken dir, Herr
With this New Year we   raise new songs To   praise the Lord with

Je- su Christ, dass du uns in so gros- ser G'fahr be-
hearts and tongues, For His sup- port in troubles past, Where-

hü- tet hast lang' Zeit und Jahr; dass du uns in so
with our life was o- ver- cast; For His sup- port in

gros- ser G'fahr be- hü- tet hast lang' Zeit und Jahr.
trou- bles past, Where- with our life was o- ver- cast.

No. 25   DAS NEUGEBORNE KINDELEIN

Cantata 122 Das neugeborne Kindelein (B.W. XXVI p. 40)

Hymn by Cyriacus Schneegass 1597   Melody by Melchior Vulpius 1609
Translation by C. Sanford Terry

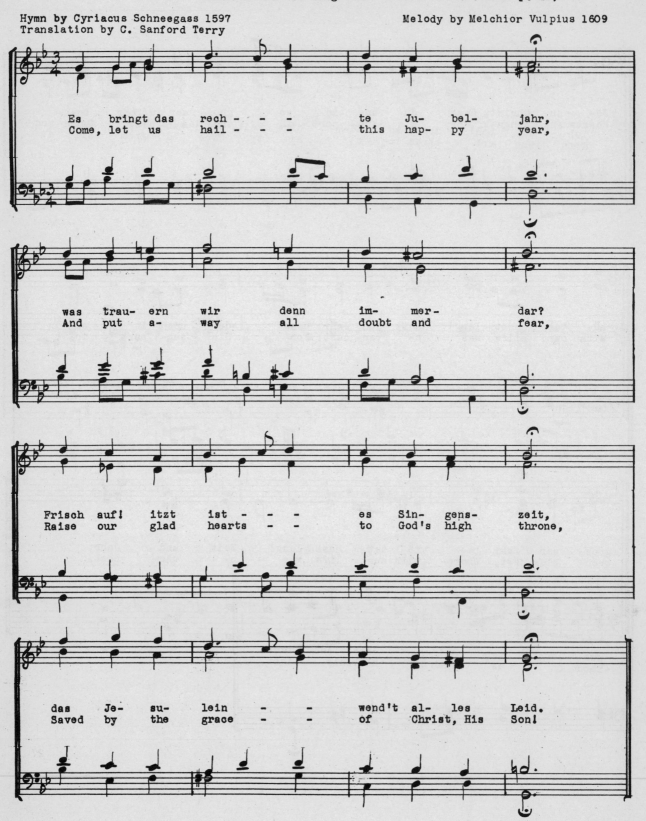

Es bringt das rech - - - te Ju- bel- jahr,
Come, let us hail - - - this hap- py year,

was trau- ern wir denn im- mer - dar?
And put a- way all doubt and fear,

Frisch auf! itzt ist - - - es Sin- gens- zeit,
Raise our glad hearts - - to God's high throne,

das Je- su- lein - - wend't al- les Leid.
Saved by the grace - - of Christ, His Son!

DER DU BIST DREI IN EINIGKEIT
(B.W. XXXIX p. 196)

Hymn by Martin Luther 1543
Translation by Richard Massie   Melody by Hermann Schein 1627

Der   du   bist   drei in   Ei-   nig- keit, ein wah- rer   Gott von
Thou   who art   three in   u-   ni-   ty, True God   from   all e-

E-   wig- keit,   die   Sonn' mit dem Tag   von uns weicht, lass
ter- ni- ty,   The   sun   is   fad- ing   from our sight, Shine

uns leuch- ten   dein   gött- lich Licht.
Thou on   us   with   heavenly light.

No. 27 DIE SONN' HAT SICH MIT IHREM GLANZ

(B.W. XXXIX p. 198)

Hymn by Josua Stegmann 1630
Translation by William Kimmel

Melody from French Psalm Book 1542

Die Sonn' hat sich mit ih- rem Glanz ge- wen- det und,
The fad- ing sun has from the heav'ns de- scend- ed, Its

was sie soll, auf die- sen Tag voll- en- det; die
rad- iant glow, that was the day has end- ed. Night's

dun- kle Nacht dringt al- lent- hal- ben zu, bringt Menschen,
shad- ows move se- rene- ly to the West, And bring to

Vieh und al- le Welt zur Ruh'.
man and all the world, Sweet rest.

No. 28   DIES SIND DIE HEIL'GEN ZEHN GEBOT'
(B.W. XXXIX, p. 198)

Hymn by Martin Luther 1524
Translation by Richard Massie

Melody from Erfurt Enchiridion 1524

Diess   sind   die heil'- gen zehn Ge- bot', die   uns   gab un-   ser
That   man   a   God- ly life might live, God   did these ten com-

Her-   re Gott durch Mo-   se, sei- nen   Die- ner treu, hoch
mand- ments give By   his   true ser- vant, Mos- es, high Up-

auf   dem Berg Si- na- i. Ky- rie e- leis!
on   the mount Si- na- i   Have mer- cy, Lord.

29

Hymn by Bartholomäus Crasselius 1697
Translation by Catherine Winkworth

Melody by J. S. Bach 1736

Dir, dir, - Je- ho- va, will - ich sin- gen,
Dir will - ich meine Lie - der brin- gen;
Je- ho- vah let me now a- dore Thee,
With songs - I fain would come - be- fore Thee;

denn wo ist doch ein sol- cher Gott, wie du?
ach gib mir dei- nes Gei- stes Kraft dar- zu,
For where is there a God, such, Lord, as Thou?
Oh let Thy Spirit deign to teach me now

dass ich - es thu' im Na- men Je- su
To praise - Thee in His name, through whom a-

Christ, so wie es dir durch ihn ge-fäl-lig ist.
lone Our songs can please Thee, Through Thy bless- ed Son.

No. 30   DU FRIEDEFÜRST, HERR JESU CHRIST.
          Cantata 67 Halt' im Gedächtniss Jesum Christ (B.W. XVI 246)

Hymn by Jacob Ebert 1601   Melody by Bartholomäus Gesius 1601
Translation by Catherine Winkworth

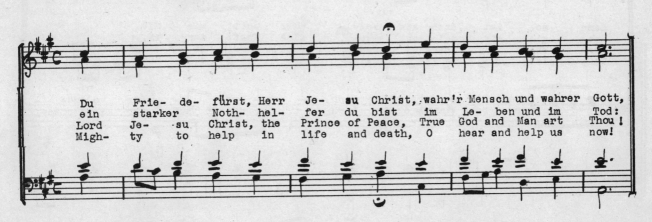

Du   Frie-de-fürst, Herr Je-su Christ, wahr'r Mensch und wahrer Gott,
ein   starker Noth-hel-fer du bist im Le- ben und im Tod:
Lord   Je- su Christ, the Prince of Peace, True God and Man art Thou!
Migh-   ty to help in life and death, O hear and help us now!

drum   wir al-lein im Na-men dein zu dei-nem Va-
'Tis   through Thy name a-bove we claim The mer-cy of

31

Thy -ter schrei- en.
Thy - Fa- ther!

No. 31   DU GROSSER SCHMERZENSMANN

(B.W. XXXIX p. 199)

Hymn by Adam Thebesius c. 1652
Translation by Elvera Wonderlich

Melody by M. Janus 1663

Du gross- er Schmerzens- mann, vom Va- ter so ge-
In sor- row Thou, o Lord didst suf- fer sore chas-

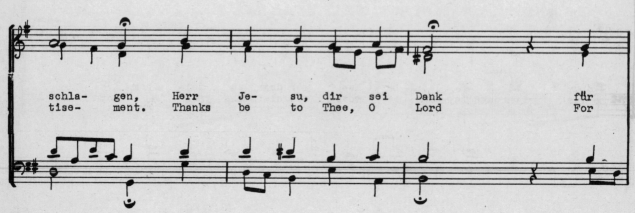

schla- gen, Herr Je- su, dir sei Dank für
tise- ment. Thanks be to Thee, O Lord For

al- le dei- ne Pla- gen: für dei- ne See- len-
ev- 'ry pain and tor- ment, For a- go- ny and

angst, für dei- ne Band' und' Noth, für
woe And ev'- ry tor- tured breath Thou

dei- ne Geis- se- lung, für dei- nen bittern Tod.
suf- fered here be- low, And for Thy cru- el death.

Cantata 18 Ich will den Kreuzstab gerne tragen (B.W. XII² 104)

Hymn by Johann Franck 1649   Melody by Johann Crüger 1649
Translation by Catherine Winkworth

Komm, o Tod, du Schla-fes Bru- der, komm, und ge
lö- se mei- nes Schiffleins Ru- der, brin- ge
Come, O Death, thou twin of sleep Lead me
Loose my rud- der, through the deep Guide my

füh- re mich nur fort; Es mag, wer da will, dich
mich an si- chern Port. du kannst mich viel- mehr er-
hence, I pray thee come, Thy ap- proach who will
ves- sel safe- ly home. 'Twere a joy to me

scheu- en, denn durch dich komm' ich hin- ein zu dem schön- sten
freu- en; Death but opes the gates to Thee, Je- sus, dear- est
to die,

Je- su- lein.
Friend to me!

No. 33   DU, O SCHÖNES WELTGEBÄUDE

(B.W. XXXIX p. 200)

Hymn by Johann Franck 1649
Translation by Catherine Winkworth

Melody by Johann Crüger 1649

Du,   o   schö-nes   Welt-ge-bäu-   de,   magst ge-   fal-len, wem du willt,
dei- ne schein-bar-li- che Freu-   de   ist mit   lau-ter Angst umhüllt.
Let   who will in   Thee   re-   joice, O Thou fair and wondrous earth!
Ev-   er an-gui-shed sor-   row's   voice Pierces through thy seeming mirth;

De-   nen,   die den   Him-mel has-   sen,   will   ich
Let   Thy vain de-   lights be giv-   en   Un-   to

ih- re   Welt- lust las-   sen;   mich verl- langt nach
them who love   not   Hea-   ven,   My de-   sire is

dir   al- lein,   al- ler- schön-ster Je- su mein.
fix'd on   Thee,   Je- sus, dear-est far to me!

35

Cantata 18 Gleich wie der Regen und Schnee (B.W. II p. 252)

Hymn by Lazarus Spengler 1524   Melody from Klug's Geistliche Lieder 1535
Translation by J.C. Jacobi

Ich bitt' o Herr, aus Her- zens Grund, du wollst nicht von   mir
dein heil'ges Wort aus mei- nem Mund; so wird mich nicht be-
I   send my cries un-to the Lord; My heart im- plores His

neh-   men   mein' Sünd und Schuld, denn in dein' Huld setz'
schä   men.
fa-   vor: That   sin and shame May lose the claim To
sa-   vor;

ich all mein Ver- trau- en, Wer sich nur   fest da-
hin- der my sal- va- tion; In Christ, the   scope Of

rauf ver- lässt, der wird den Tod nicht schau- -   en.
all my hope, I 'scape death and dam- na- -   tion.

Cantata 80 Ein' feste Burg ist unser Gott. (B.W. XVIII p. 378)

Hymn by Martin Luther 1527
Translation by Catherine Winkworth

Melody by Martin Luther 1527

Hymn by Erhart Hagenwalt 1524   Melody from Walter's Geystliche gesangk Buchleyn 1524
Translation by J.C. Jacobi

Er-   barm' dich mein, o Her-   re Gott, nach
wasch'   ab; mach' rein mein' Mis-   se- that, ich
Show   pi- ty, Lord! O mer- cies large for- give! Let
Are   not thy   and free? May

dei- ner gross'n Barm-her-zig- keit,   Al-   lein ich   dir ge-
kenn' mein' Sünd, und ist mir leid.   O   wash my   soul from
a   re- pent-ing reb-el live!
not   a   sin- ner trust in Thee?

sün-   digt hab, das ist wi- der mich ste- tig- lich; das
ev-   'ry sin, And make my guil-ty con- science clean; Here

38

Bös' vor dir nicht mag be-stah'n, du bleibst- ge-
on my heart the bur-den lies, And past-- of-

recht, ob man ur-thei-le dich.
fen-ces pain ur-mine eyes.

No. 37 ERHALT' UNS HERR, BEI DEINEM WORT

Cantata 6 Bleib bei uns, denn es will Abend werden. (B.W. I p. 176)

Hymn by Martin Luther 1541   Melody from Klug's Geistliche Lieder 1535
Translation by Catherine Winkworth

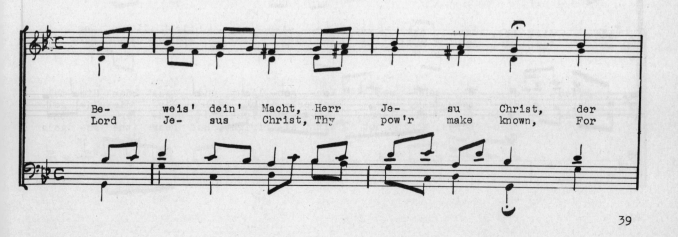

Be- weis' dein' Macht, Herr Je- su Christ, der
Lord Je- sus Christ, Thy pow'r make known, For

du   Herr   al-   ler   Her-   ren bist: be-   schirm' dein' ar- me
Thou art   Lord of   Her-   lords a-   lone; De-   fend Thy Christen-

Chris- ten-   heit, dass   sie   dich lob' in   E-   wig-   keit.
dom,   that   we   May   ev-   er- more   sing praise to Thee.

No. 38   ERMUNTRE DICH, MEIN SCHWACHER GEIST

Christmas Oratorio (B.W. V² p. 59)

Hymn by Johann Rist 1641   Melody by Johann Schop 1641
Translation by J. Troutbeck

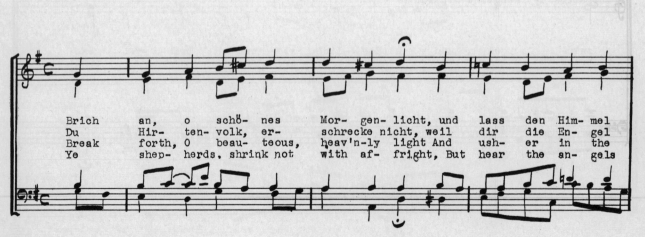

Brich   an,   o   schö- nes   Mor- gen- licht, und   lass   den Him- mel
Du   Hir-   ten- volk,   er-   schrecke nicht, weil dir   die En- gel
Break   forth, O   beau-   teous, heav'n-ly light And   ush-   er   in   the
Ye   shep- herds, shrink not   with af- fright, But hear   the an- gels

ta- gen!
sa- gen: dass die- ses schwache Knäbe- lein soll
morn- ing;
warn- ing. This Child, now weak in in- fan- cy, Our

un- ser Trost und Freu- de sein, da- zu den Sa- tan
con- fi- dence and joy shall be, The pow'r of Sa- tan

zwin- gen und letzt- lich Frie- den brin- gen.
break- ing, Our peace e- ter- nal mak- ing.

Cantata 11 Lobet Gott in seinen Reichen (B.W. II, p. 32)

Hymn by Johann Rist 1641
Translation by C.S. Terry

Melody by Johann Schop 1641

Nun lie-get al- les un- ter dir, dich
Die En-gel müs-sen für und für dir
Prone at Thy feet cre-a-tion lies, Thy
An-gel-ic hosts haste through the skies, Thy

selbst nur aus-ge-nom-men;
auf-zu-war-ten kom-men.
sovereign will o-bey-ing.
dread commands o-bey-ing.

Die Für-sten stehn auch auf der Bahn,
Princes and kings be-fore Thee bow,

und sind dir wil-lig un-ter-than; Luft,
All Thy dread pow-er and might al-low; Earth,

Was- ser, Feu'r und Er- den muss
heav- en, fire, and o- cean Lie

dir zu Dien- ste wer- den.
pros- trate in de- vo- tion.

No. 40   ERSCHIENEN IST DER HERRLICH' TAG

Cantata 67 Halt im Gedächtniss Jesum Christ (B.W. XVI p. 233)

Hymn by Nicolaus Herman 1560   Melody by Nicolaus Herman 1560
Translation by Elvera Wonderlich

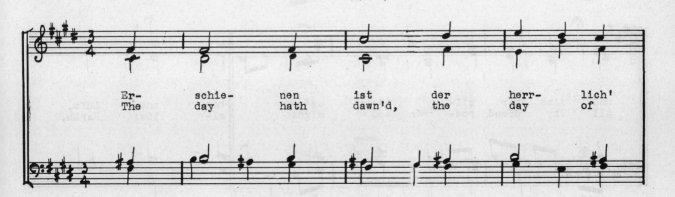

Er- schie- nen ist der herr- lich'
The day hath dawn'd, the day of

Tag,   d'ran sich   Nie- mand   g'nug   freu-   en
days,   So   let   us   sing   our   fer-   vent

mag: Christ, un-   ser   Herr,   heut'   tri- um-
praise, For   Christ,   our   Lord,   has   tri- umphed to-

phirt,   all'   sein'   Feind'   er   ge-   fangen
day;   His   en-   e-   mies   are   cast   a-

führt.   Al-   le- lu-   ja!
way.   Al-   le- lu-   ja!

Cantata 145 So du mit deinem Mund. (B.W. XXX p. 122)

Hymn by Nicolaus Herman 1560
Translation by Catherine Winkworth

Melody by Nicolaus Herman 1560

Cantata 86 Wahrlich, ich sage euch. (B.W. XX¹ p. 134)

Hymn by Paulus Speratus 1523   Melody from Etlich Christliche Lyeder 1524
Translation by Henry Mills

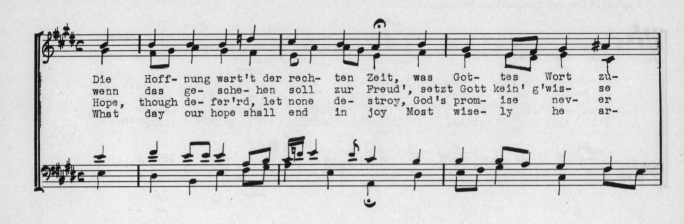

Die   Hoff- nung wart't der rech- ten Zeit, was Got- tes Wort zu-se-
wenn   das   ge- sche- hen soll   zur Freud', setzt Gott kein' g'wis-se
Hope, though de- fer'rd, let none de- stroy, God's prom- ise   nev- er
What   day   our hope shall end   in   joy Most wise- ly   he ar-

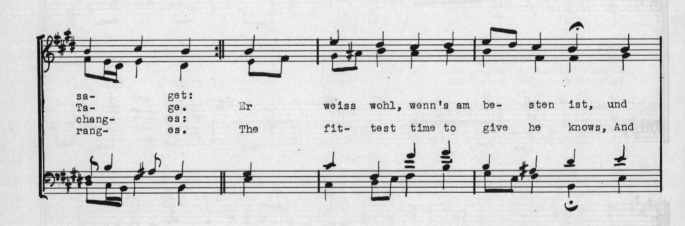

sa-   get:
Ta-   ge.   Er   weiss wohl, wenn's am be- sten ist, und
chang-   es: The   fit- test time to give he knows, And
rang-   es.

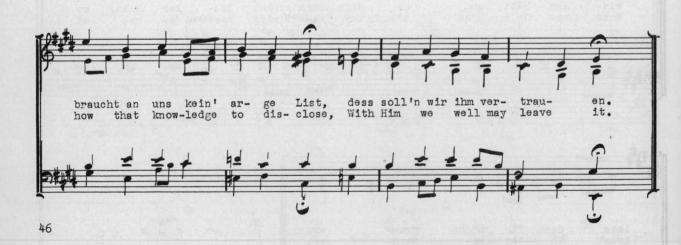

braucht an uns kein' ar- ge List, dess soll'n wir ihm ver- trau- en.
how   that know-ledge to dis- close, With Him we well may leave it.

No. 43   ES IST DAS HEIL UNS KOMMEN HER

Cantata 9 Es ist das Heil uns kommen her. (B.W. I p. 274)

Hymn by Paulus Speratus 1523
Translation by J.C. Jacobi

Melody from Etlich Christliche Lyeder 1524

Ob   sich's   an- liess', als   wollt' er   nicht,   lass
Denn   wo   er   ist   am   be-   sten   mit,   da
Be   not   cast down   when   He   de-   lays   To
He   then   is   near- est   when   thy   ways   Seem

dich   es nicht er-   schre-   cken,   sein   Wort lass dir ge-
will   er's nicht ent- de-   cken;   soin
crown thine ex- pec- ta-   tion;   On   His   e-   ter- nal
full   of des-o- la-   tion.

wis-   ser   sein, und   ob   dein Herz sprach lau-   ter Nein, so
Word   re-   ly,   E'en   though thy wa- v'ring heart de- ny;   And

lass   doch   dir   nicht   grau-   en.
trust in   thy   Re-   deem-   er.

47

Cantata 155 Mein Gott, wie lang', ach lange. (B.W. XXXII p. 96)

Hymn by Paulus Speratus 1523
Translation by J.C. Jacobi

Melody from Etlich Christliche Lyeder 1524

Ob   sich's   an-   liess',   als   wollt'   er   nicht,   lass
denn   wo   er   ist   am   be-   sten   mit,   da
Be   not   cast   down   when   He   de-   lays   To
He   then   is   near-   est,   when   thy   ways   Seem

dich   es   nicht   er-   schre-   cken,
will   er's   nicht   ent-   de-   cken;   sein   Wort   lass   dir   ge-
crown   thine   ex-   pec-   ta-   tion.
full   of   des-   o-   la-   tion.   On   His   e-   ter-   nal

wis-   ser   sein,   und   ob   dein   Herz   spräch'   lau-   ter   Nein,   so
Word   re-   ly,   E'en   though   thy   wa-   v'ring   heart   de-   ny;   And

lass   doch   dir   nicht   grau-   en.
trust   in   thy   re-   deem-   er.

48

Hymn by Franz Burmeister 1662

Translation by Charles N. Boyd

Melody by Johann Ahle 1662

Es ist ge- nug: Herr, wenn es dir ge- fällt, so
It is e- nough! Lord, by Thy wise de- cree I

span- ne mich doch aus. Mein Je- sus kommt: nun gu- te
gird me to de- part. My Je- sus comes! Fare-well, O

Nacht, o Welt! ich fahr' in's Him- mels- haus, ich fah- re
world, to thee; I seek my heav'n- ly home. In peace I

sich- er hin mit Frie- den, mein gros- ser
trav- el sure-ly on- ward; Be- hind is

Jam- mer bleibt dar- nie- den. Es ist ge-
earth- ly grief and sor- row; It is e-

nug, es ist ge- nug.
nough, it is e- nough!

Hymn by Paul Gerhardt 1653
Translation by J. Troutbeck

Melody from Klug's Geistliche Lieder 1535

51

Hymn by Martin Luther c. 1518   Melody from Walter's Geystliche gesangk Buchleyn 1524
Translation by Richard Massie

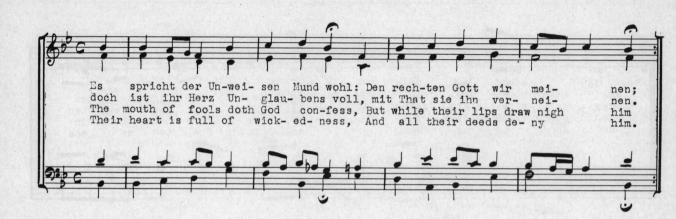

Es spricht der Un-wei-sen Mund wohl: Den rech-ten Gott wir mei- nen;
doch ist ihr Herz Un-glau- bens voll, mit That sie ihn ver- nei- nen.
The mouth of fools doth God con-fess, But while their lips draw nigh him.
Their heart is full of wick- ed- ness, And all their deeds de- ny him.

Ihr We- sen ist ver- der- bet zwar, für Gott ist es ein
Cor- rupt are they, and ev- 'ry one A- bom- i- na- ble

Greu- el gar, es thut Ihr' Kei- ner kein Gut.
deeds hath done; There is not one well- do- er.

(B.W. XXXIX p. 204)

Hymn by Ludwig Helmbold 1585   Melody from Burck's Dreissig Geistliche Lieder 1594
Translation by Elvera Wonderlich

(B.W. XXXIX p. 205)

Hymn by Michael Weisse 1531
Translation by C.S. Terry

Melody by Michael Weisse 1531

Es   wird   schier der   letz- te   Tag   her-   kom-   men,
Day of   doom, the   Lord's great day ap-   proach-   eth,

denn   die   Bos- heit   hat   sehr   zu- ge-   nom-   men;
When   to   judge the   world   in   wrath He   com-   eth.

was   Chri-   stus hat   vor   ge-   sagt,   das   wird   jetzt be-   klagt.
Lo,   the   hour that   Christ did   tell   Calls   to   heav'n or   hell!

54

No. 50   ES WOLL UNS GOTT GENÄDIG SEIN

(B.W. XXXIX p. 205)

Hymn by Martin Luther 1524
Translation by Arthur Tozer Russell

Melody from Strassburger Kirchenamt 1525

Es woll' uns Gott ge- nä- - - dig sein und
sein Ant- litz uns mit hel- - - lem Schein er-
May God un- to us gra- - - cious be, And
Lord show Thy face un- to us through Thee E-

sei- nen Se- gen ge- - - - ben;
leucht' zum ew'- gen Le- - - - ben,
grant to us His bless- - - - ing;
ter- nal life pos- sess- - - - ing:

dass
dass
That
That

wir er- ken- nen sei- ne Werk! und, was ihn liebt, auf
all Thy work and will, O God, To us may be re-

55

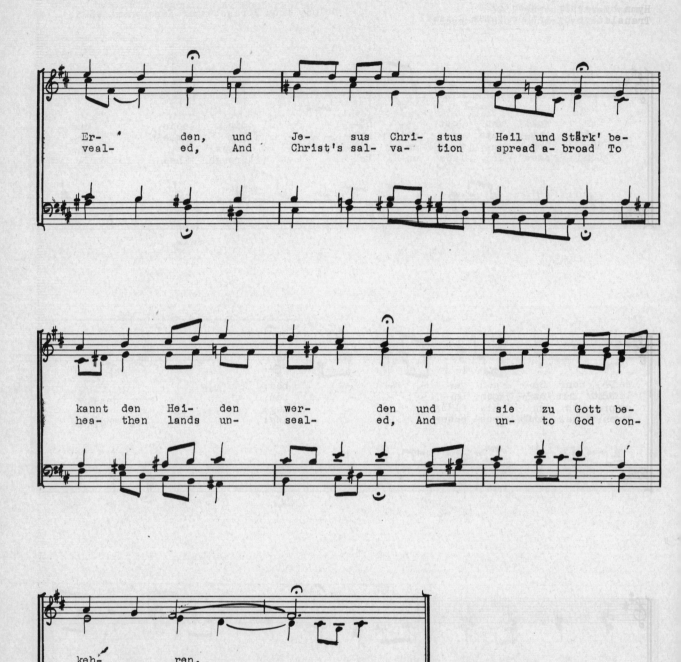

Er   veal-   den,   und   Je-   sus   Chri- stus   Heil und Stärk' be-
    veal-   ed,   And Christ's sal- va- tion   spread a- broad To

kannt den Hei- den   wer-   den und   sie   zu Gott be-
hea- then lands un-   seal-   ed, And   un- to God con-

keh-   ren.
vert   them.

Cantata 69 Lobe den Herrn, meine Seele (B.W. XVI p. 325)

Hymn by Martin Luther 1524
Translation by Arthur Tozer Russell

Melody from Strassburger Kirchenamt 1525

Es dan- ke, Gott, und lo- - - be dich das
Land bringt Frucht und bes- - - sert sich, dein
Thy fold, O God, shall bring - - to Thee The
word shall rich- ly fruit- -. ful be, And

Volk in gu- ten Tha- - - - ten. Das
Wort ist wohl ge- ra- - - - ing; Thy
praise of ho- ly liv- - - - ing; Thy
earth shall yield thanks-giv- - - - then. Uns
ing. Bless

seg- ne Va- ter und der Sohn, uns seg- ne Gott, der
us, O Fa- ther! bless, O Son! Grant, Ho- ly Ghost, Thy

* (Chord third appears in instrumental accompaniment)

heil'- ge Geist, dem al- le Welt die Eh- re thu', vor
bless- -ing! Thee earth shall hon- or-- Thee a- lone, Thy

ihm sich fürch- te al- ler- meist, und
fear all souls pos- sess- -ing. Now

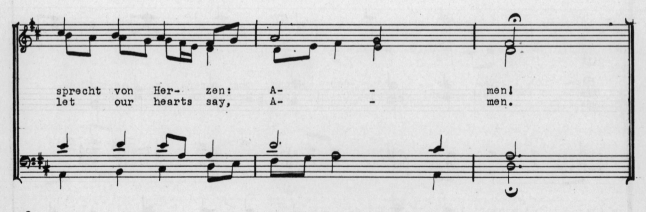

sprecht von Her- zen: A- - men!
let our hearts say, A- - men.

Cantata 19 Es erhub sich ein Streit (B. W. II p. 288)

Hymn from Demantius's Threnodiae 1620
Translation by C. Sanford Terry

Melody from French Psalter 1551

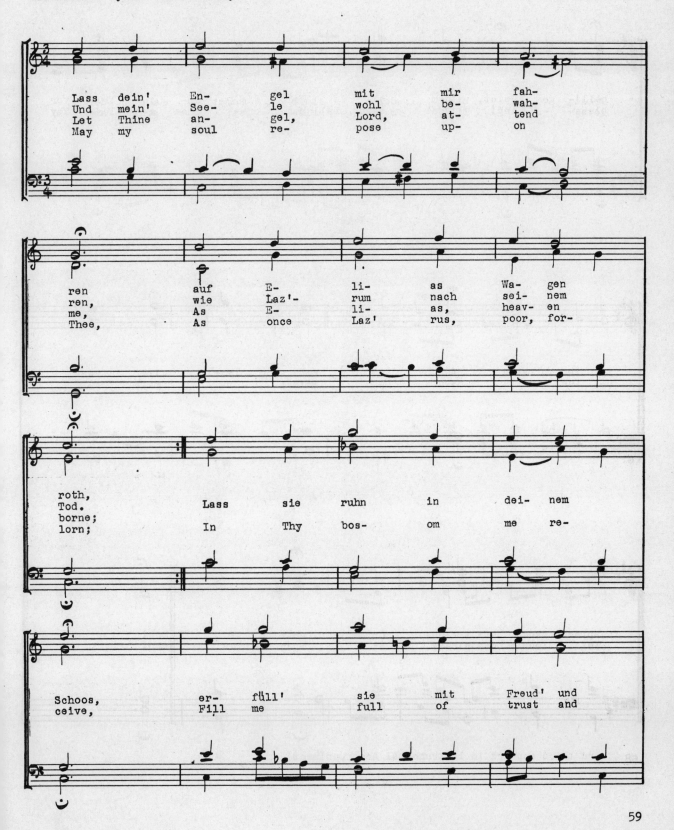

Lass dein' En- gel mit mir fah-
Und mein' See- le, wohl be- wah-tend
Let Thine an- gel Lord, pose up-
May my soul re- pose up- on

ren, auf E- li- as Wa- gen
ren, wie Laz'- rum nach sei- nem
me, As E- li- as, heav- en
Thee, As once Laz' rus, poor, for-

roth, Lass sie ruhn in dei- nem
Tod.
borne; In Thy bos- om me re-
lorn;

Schoos, er- füll' sie mit Freud' und
ceive, Fill me full of trust and

Trost,   bis   der   Leib   kommt   aus   der
love,   Till   my   ris-   en   soul   and

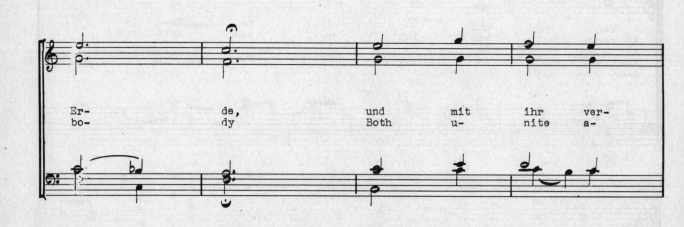

Er-   de,   und   mit   ihr   ver-
bo-   dy   Both   u-   nite   a-

ei-   nigt   wer-   de.
bove   in   glo-   ry!

* (Chord third appears in instrumental accompaniment)

Cantata 25 Es ist nichts Gesundes an meinem Leibe (B.W. V^1 p. 188)

Hymn by Johann Heermann 1630   Melody from French Psalter 1551
Translation by C. Sanford Terry

Ich will al- le mei- ne Ta- ge rüh- men dei- ne
dass du mei- ne Plag' und Kla- ge hast so herz- lich
All my days, O God, I'll praise Thee, And Thy might- y
Care and sor- row flee be- fore Thee, Cap- tives of Thy

star- ke Hand,
ab- ge- wandt. Nicht nur in der Sterb- lich- keit
arm ac- claim.
glo- rious Name. Lord, Thy prais- es will I sound

soll dein Ruhm sein aus- ge- breit't: ich will's auch her-
While there's breath with- in me found, And here- af- ter

nach er- wei- sen, und dort e- wig- lich dich prei- sen.
shall my spir- it Still pro- claim Thy won- drous mer- it.

No. 54   FREU' DICH SEHR, O MEINE SEELE

Cantata 39 Brich dem Hungrigen dein Brod (B.W. VII p. 348)

Hymn by David Denicke c. 1648
Translation by C. Sanford Terry

Melody from French Psalter 1551

Se-   lig sind, die aus Er- bar- men   sich an-   neh- men
sind mit- lei- dig   mit den Ar- men, bit- ten   treu- lich
Blest are they whose founts of mer- cy Free- ly for an-
To   the poor their alms dis- burse they, Pray- ing God to

frem- der Noth,   Die be- hülf- lich sind mit Rath,
für   sie Gott.   Who the help- less aids with word,
oth- er flow,
heal their woe.

auch, wo mög- lich, mit der That,   wer- den wie- der
Or   to gen- 'rous acts is stirred, Shall him- self God's

Hülf em- pfan-   gen,   und Barm- her- zig- keit er- lan- gen.
hand be giv-   en,   Stretched to lead him up to heav- en.

62

No. 55 FREUET EUCH, IHR CHRISTEN

Cantata 40 Dazu ist erschienen der Sohn Gottes (B.W. VII p. 394)

Hymn by Christian Keimann 1646   Melody from Hammerschmidt's Musicalische Andachten 1646
Translation by Catherine Winkworth

Je- su, nimm dich dei- ner Glie- der fer- ner in Ge-
Je- su, guard and guide Thy mem- bers, Fill Thy breth- 'ren

na- den an; schen- ke, was man bit- ten kann,
with Thy grace, Hear their pray'rs in ev— 'ry place,

zu er- qui- cken dei- ne Brü- der: gieb der gan- zen
Quick- en now life's faint- est em- bers; Grant all Chris- tians,

Chris- ten- schaar, Frie- den und ein sel'- ges Jahr!
far and near, Ho- ly peace, a glad New Year!

Freu- de, Freu- de ü- ber Freu- de! Chri- stus wehr- et
Joy, O joy be- yond all glad- ness! Christ hath done a-

al- lem Lei- de. Won- ne, Won- ne ü- ber Won- ne!
way with sad- ness! Hence, all sor- row, all re- pin- ing,

er ist die Ge- na- den- son- ne.
For the Sun of grace is shin- .ing.

(B.W. XXXIX p. 206)

Hymn by Casperl Peltsch 1648   Melody from Riemann's Sammlung
Translation by Elvera Wonderlich   alter und neuer Melodien 1747

Für   Freu- den lasst uns   sprin-   gen,   ihr   Chri- sten all- zu-
Mit   Mund und Her- zen   sin-   gen,   denn   Christ vom Him- mel-
Re-   joice ye Christ- ians loud-   ly,   This   day   to praise be
With   ar- dent voice sing   proud-   ly,   Pro-   claim that Christ from

glei-   che!
rei-   che   von   ei- ner   Jung- frau   ist   ge- bor'n, wer
giv-   en;   Is   born this   day in   Beth- le- hem, Pro-
heav-   en   Is   born this   day in   Beth- le- hem, Pro-

hat   zu- vor ge   hört von   sol-   chen   Din-   gen?
claim to   all on   earth This won-   drous sto-   ry.

Cantata 64 Sehet, welch' eine Liebe (B.W. XVI p. 118)

Hymn by Martin Luther 1524   Melody from Walter's Geistliche gesangk Buchleyn 1524
Translation by Richard Massie

Das   hat er Al- les uns ge- than,   sein' gross' Lieb' zu zei- gen an. Dess
All   this He did that He might prove To us sin- ners His great love; For

freu' sich al-   le   Chri- sten- heit und   dank' ihm   dess   in
'this let Chris- ten- dom a-   dore. And   praise His name   for-

E-   wig- keit. —   —   Ky- rie- leis!
ev-   er-   more. —   —   Ky- rie- leis.

66

GELOBET SEIST DU, JESU CHRIST

(B.W. XXXIX p. 207)

Hymn by Martin Luther 1524
Translation by Richard Massie

Melody from Walter's Geistliche gesangk Buchleyn 1524

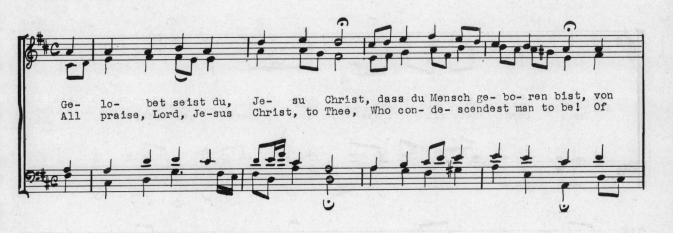

Ge- lo- bet seist du, Je- su Christ, dass du Mensch ge- bo- ren bist, von
All praise, Lord, Je-sus Christ, to Thee, Who con- de- scendest man to be! Of

ei- ner Jung- frau das ist wahr, des freu- et sich der
Vir- gin- moth- er born on earth, The an- gels cel- e-

En- - - gel Schar. Al- le- lu- ja!
brate Thy - birth. Al- le- lu- ja!

Christmas Oratorio (B.W. V² p. 110)

Hymn by Martin Luther 1524
Translation by J. Troutbeck

Melody from Walter's Geistliche gesangk Buchleyn 1524

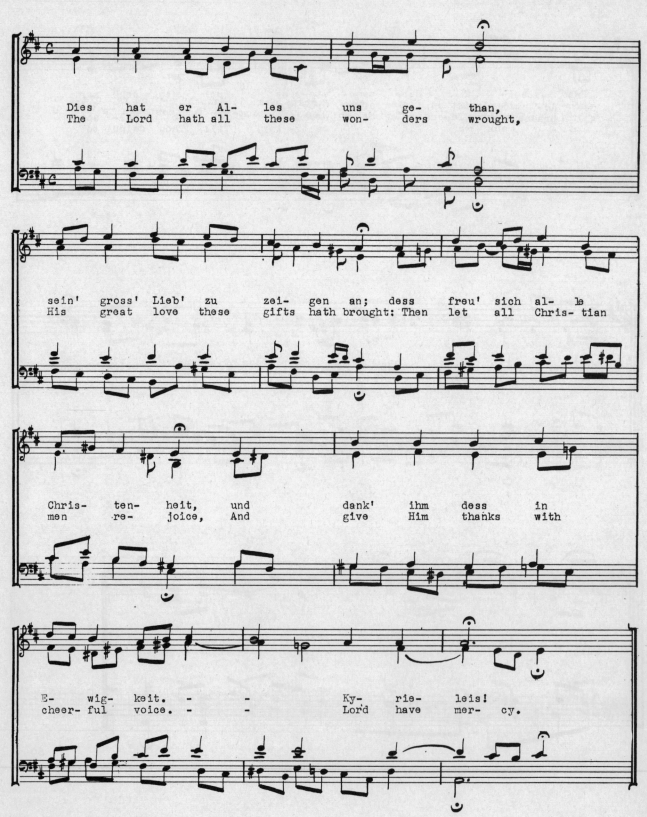

Dies   hat   er Al- les   uns   ge-   than,
The   Lord hath all these won- ders   wrought,

sein' gross' Lieb' zu   zei- gen an; dess freu' sich al- le
His   great love these gifts hath brought: Then let   all Chris-tian

Chris- ten-   heit,   und   dank' ihm dess   in
men   re-   joice, And   give Him thanks with

E- wig- keit. - -   Ky- rie- leis!
cheer- ful voice. - -   Lord have mer- cy.

Hymn by Heinrich Alberti 1643
Translation by J. Troutbeck

Melody by Heinrich Alberti 1642

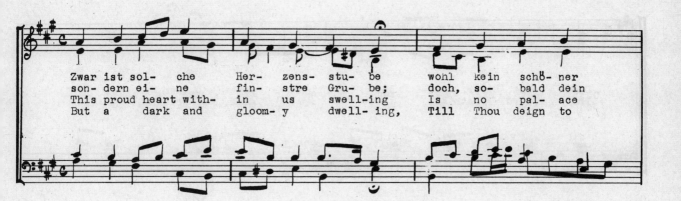

Zwar ist sol- che Her- zens- stu- be wohl kein schö- ner
son- dern ei- ne fin- stre Gru- be; doch, so- bald dein
This proud heart with- in us swell- ing Is no pal- ace
But a dark and gloom- y dwell- ing, Till Thou deign to

Für- sten- saal, in die- sel- be nur wird blin- ken,
Gna- den- strahl
rich and fair, When Thy grace with- in it beam- eth,
en- ter there.

wird sie vol- ler Son- nen dün- ken.
Full of heav'n- ly light it seem- eth.

Hymn by Erasmus Alberus 1548
Translation by C. Warren Fox

Melody by Erasmus Alberus 1549

Gott hat das E- van- gel- li- um ge- ge-
God gave the Gos- pel un- to men To

ge- ben, dass wir wer- den fromm; die Welt acht' sol- chen
bring them close to Him a- gain. This treas- ure men do

Schatz nicht hoch, der meh- rer' Theil fragt nichts dar- nach, das
not es- teem, Nor let God's Word their souls re- deem. Be-

ist ein Zei- chen vor dem jüng- sten Tag.
yond their sight The fires of judg- ment gleam.

Hymn by Martin Luther 1524   Melody from Walter's Geistliche gesangk Buchleyn 1524
Translation by Richard Massie

heil' gen Leich- nam, der von dei- ner Mutt'r Ma-
bo- dy, Lord, the same Which from Thine own moth- er

ri- a kam, und das hei- li- ge Blut
Ma- ry came By the drops Thou didst bleed,

hilf uns Herr, aus al- ler Noth. Ky- rie e-
Help us in the hour of need! Ky- rie e-

lei- - - - son.
lei- - - - son.

Cantata 96 Herr Christ, der einig Gott's Sohn (B.W. XXII p. 184)

Hymn by Elizabeth Cruciger 1524   Melody from Erfurt Enchiridion 1524
Translation by Myles Coverdale

Er tödt' uns durch dein' Gü-   te, er- weck' uns durch dein'
den al- ten Men- schen krän-   ke, dass der neu' le- ben
A- wake us, Lord, we pray Thee; That our new man may

Gnad';
mag   wohl   hier   auf die- ser   Er-   den, den
give,
live. So   will we al- ways   thank   Thee, That

Sinn und all' Be- gehr- en   und G'dan- ken hab'n zu   dir.
show'st us so great mer- cy,   And our sons dost for- give.

73

(B.W. XXXIX p. 213)

Hymn adapted from Dicimus grates tibi by
    Paul Eber c. 1554
Translation by J.C. Jacobi

Melody from French Psalter 1551

Herr   Gott,   dich   lo-   ben   al- le   wir   und
To   God,   let   all   the   hu- man   race   Bring

sol-   len   bil-   lig   dan- ken   dir,   für
hum-   ble   wor-   ship   mixed with   grace,   Who

dein   Ge-   schöpf   der   En- gel   schon,   die
makes   His   love   and   Enwis.- dom   known   By

um   dich   schweb'n   in   dei- nem   Thron.
an-   gels   that   sur- round   His   throne.

Hymn by Johann Franck 1649
Translation by Catherine Winkworth

Melody by Johann Crüger 1649

Herr, ich ha- be miss- ge- han- delt, ja mich
ich bin nicht den Weg ge- wan- delt, den du
Lord to Thee I make con- fes- sion, I have
I have mul- ti- plied trans- gres- sion, Cho- sen

drückt der Sün- den Last; und itzt wollt' ich gern aus Schre-
mir ge- zei- get hast;
sinn'd and gone a- stray: Forced at last to see my er-
for my- self the way:

cken, mich vor dei- nem Zorn ver- ste- cken.
rors, Lord, I trem- ble at Thy ter- rors.

Cantata 48 Ich elender Mensch, wer wird mich erlösen (B.W. X p. 298)

Hymn from Schein's Cantional 1627
Translation by Charles N. Boyd

Melody from Dresden Gesangbuch 1593

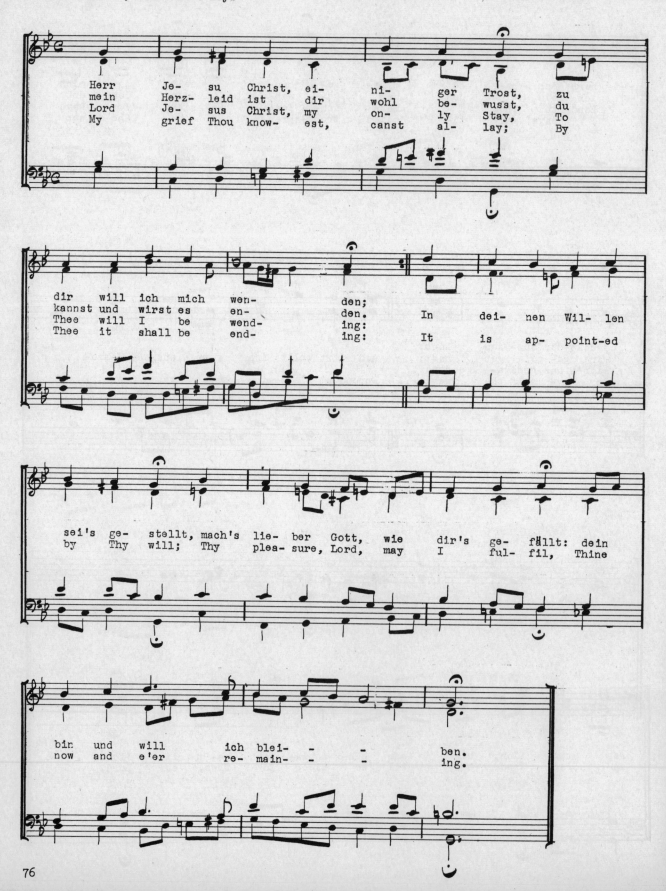

Cantata 127 Herr Jesu Christ, wahr'r Mensch und Gott (B.W. XXVI p. 160)

Hymn by Paul Eber 1557   Melody of a French psalm adapted by Johann Doles 1785
Translation by Catherine Winkworth

No. 68   HERR, NUN LASS IN FRIEDE

(B.W. XXXIX p. 219)

Hymn by David Behme c. 1663   Melody from Gesangbuch der Böhmischen Brüder 1694
Translation by Catherine Winkworth

Herr, nun lass in Frie-   de,   le- bens- satt und
Lord, now let Thy serv-   ant   Pass in peace a-

mü-   de,   dei nen Die ner   fah   ren,
way;   I have had e-   nough of life,

zu den Him mels schaa-   ren,   se- lig und im
Here I would not stay: Let me go if

Stil-   len,   doch nach dei nem   Wil-   len.
such Thy will,   With a heart at   rest and still.

St. John Passion (B.W. XII¹ p. 131)

Hymn by Martin Schalling 1567   Melody from Havs Kirchen Cantorei 1587
Translation by J. Troutbeck

Ach   Herr, lass dein lieb' En- ge- lein am letz- ten End' die
Den   Leib in sein'm Schlaf- kam- mer- lein gar sanft, ohn ein- ge
Lord   Je-   sus, Thy dear an- gel send, When- e'er my mor- tal
With- in   its nar- row cham- ber keep My bo- dy safe in

See-   le mein in A- bra- hams Schoos tra - - gen;
Qual   und Pein, ruhn bis am jüng- sten Ta - - ge!
life   shall end, And bear my soul to hea - - ven.
pain- less sleep, Till Thy last call be giv - - en.

Als-   dann vom Tod er- we- cke mich, dass mei- ne Au- gen
And   when from death Thou wak- est me, In bliss un- told mine

se-hen dich in al-ler Freud', o Got-tes Sohn, mein
eyes shall see, O Son of God, Thy glo-rious face, My

Hei-land und Ge- na-den -thron! Herr Je- su Christ, er-hö- re mich, er-
Sav-iour and my Fount of Grace. Lord Je- sus Christ, O hear Thou me, O

hö- re mich, ich will dich prei- sen e- wig-lich!
hear Thou me, Thee will I praise e- ter- nal- ly.

Cantata 153 Schau lieber Gott wie meine Feind' (B.W. XXXII p. 46)

Hymn by Paul Gerhardt 1656   Secular melody "Mein G'müt ist mir verwirrt" by
Translation by Henry Mills   Hans Leo Hassler 1601

Hymn by Paul Gerhardt 1656   Secular melody "Mein G'müt ist mir verwirrt" by
Translation by Miss H.F.H. Johnston   Hans Leo Hassler 1601

(B.W. XXXIX p. 185)

Hymn by Paul Gerhardt 1656   Secular melody "Mein G'müt ist mir verwirrt" by
Translation by Miss H.F.H. Johnston   Hans Leo Hassler 1601

Be- fiehl du dei- ne We- ge, und was dein Her- ze
der al- ler- treu-sten Pfle- ge, der den Him- mel
Com- mit thy ways to Je- sus, Thy bur- dens and thy
He from them all re- leas- es, He all thy sor- row

kränkt, Der Wol- ken, Luft und Win- den gibt
lenkt.
cares; Who gives the winds their cour- ses, And
shares.

We- ge, Lauf und Bahn, der wird auch We- ge
bounds the o- cean's shore, Will suf- fer not temp-

fin- den, die dein Fuss ge- hen kann.
ta- tion To rise be- yond Thy pow'r.

No. **73**   HERZLICH THUT MICH VERLANGEN

St. Matthew Passion (B.W. IV p. 248)

Hymn by Paul Gerhardt 1656
Translation by Miss H.F.H. Johnston

Secular melody "Mein G'müt ist mir verwirrt" by
Hans Leo Hassler 1601

St. Matthew Passion (B.W. IV p. 214)

Hymn by Paul Gerhardt 1656
Translation by John S. Dwight

Secular melody "Mein G'müt ist mir verwirrt"
by Hans Leo Hassler 1601

O Haupt voll Blut und Wun- den, voll Schmerz und vol- ler
O Haupt, zu Spott ge- bun- den mit ei- ner Dor- nen-
O Head all bruis'd and woun- ded, Hung up to bru- tal
O Head, for shame sur- roun- ded With crown of cru- el

Hohn!
kron!   O   Haupt, sonst schön ge- zie- ret   mit
scorn!
thorn!   O   Head, to hon- or won- ted,   To

höchster Ehr' und   Zier,   jetzt   a- ber hoch schim-
splendor all di- vine,   Now   out- rag'd and af-

pfi- ret: ge- grü- sset seist du   mir.
fron- ted: All Hail, dear Mas- ter   mine!

St. Matthew Passion (B.W. IV, p. 186)

Hymn by Paul Gerhardt 1656
Translation by Miss H.F.H. Johnston

Secular melody "Mein G'müt ist mir verwirrt"
by Hans Leo Hassler 1601

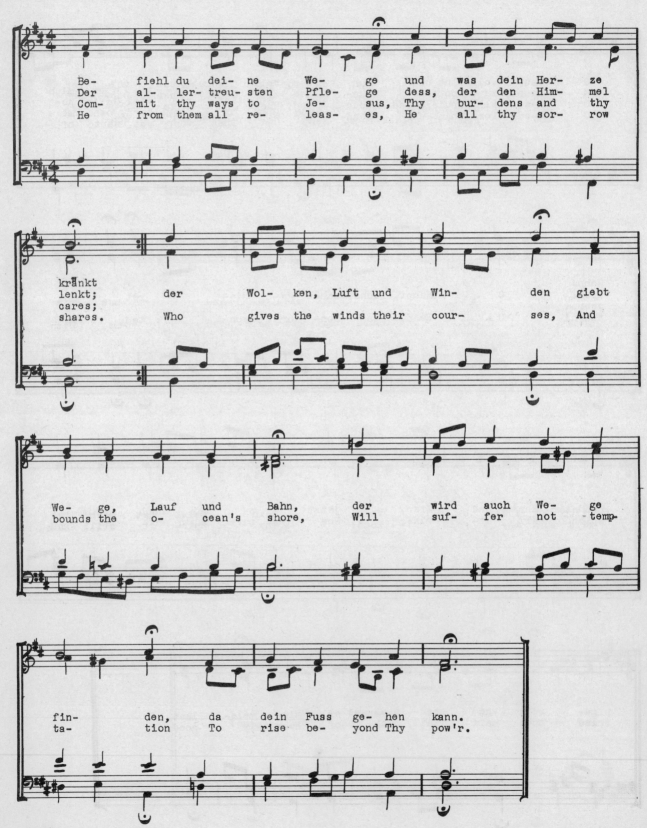

St. Matthew Passion (B.W. IV, p. 51)

Hymn by Paul Gerhardt 1656
Translation by John S. Dwight

Secular melody "Mein G'müt ist mir verwirrt"
by Hans Leo Hassler 1601.

Er- ken- ne mich, mein Hü- ter, mein Hir- te, nimm mich
Von dir, Quell al- ler Gü- ter, ist mir viel Gut's ge-
Ac- knowledge me, my Keep- er, My Shep- herd, own me
Thou fount of bless-ings, deep- er Than deep- est want of

an, Dein Mund hat mich ge- la- bet mit
than. Thine,
Thine, Thy mouth full oft hath fed me With
mine.

Milch und süss- er Kost, dein Geist hat mich be-
milk and an- gels' food; Thy Spir- it still hath

ga- bet mit manch- er Him- mels- lust.
led me The way of heav'n-ly good.

Hymn by Paul Gerhardt 1656
Translation by J. Troutbeck

Secular melody "Mein G'müt ist mir verwirrt"
by Hans Leo Hassler 1601

Wie soll ich dich em- pfan- gen, und wie be- gegn' ich
o al- ler Welt Ver- lan- gen, o mei- ner See- len
How shall I fit- ly meet Thee, And give Thee wel- come
The na- tions long to greet Thee, And I would greet Thee,

dir? O Je- su, Je- su! se- tze mir
Zier!
due?
too. O Fount of light shine bright- ly Up-

selbst die Fa- ckel bei, da- mit, was ich er-
on my dark- ened heart, That I may serve Thee

gö- tze, mir kund und wiss- end sei.
right- ly, And know Thee as Thou art.

No. 78   HERZLIEBSTER JESU, WAS HAST DU VERBROCHEN

St. Matthew Passion (B.W. IV, p. 192)

Hymn by Johann Heermann 1630   Melody by Johann Crüger 1640
Translation by John S. Dwight

Hymn by Johann Heermann 1630   Melody by Johann Crüger 1640
Translation by J. Troutbeck

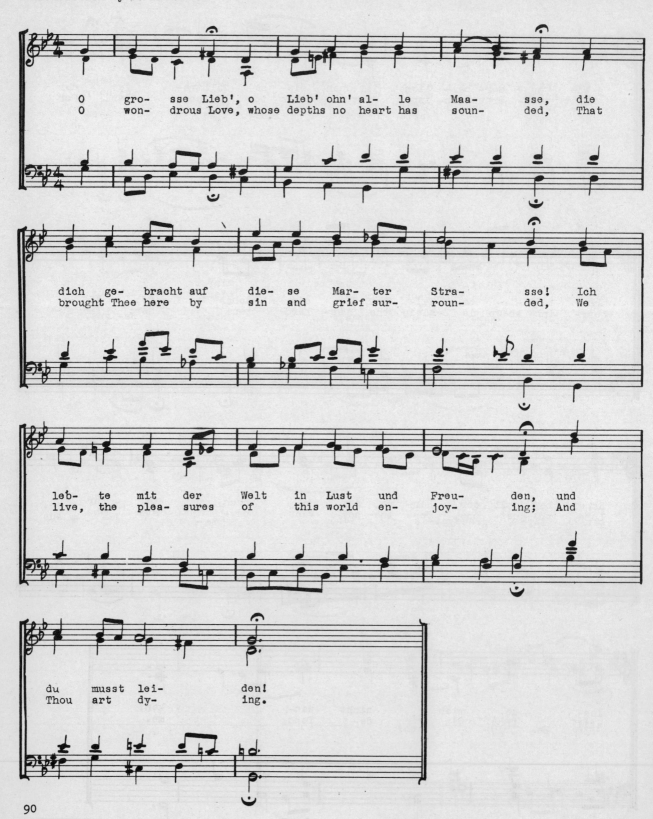

O   gro-   sse Lieb', o   Lieb' ohn' al- le   Maa-   sse, die
O   won-   drous Love, whose depths no heart has soun-   ded, That

dich ge- bracht auf die- se   Mar- ter Stra-   sse! Ich
brought Thee here by   sin and   grief sur- roun-   ded, We

leb- te mit der   Welt   in   Lust und   Freu-   den, und
live, the plea- sures of   this world en-   joy-   ing; And

du   musst lei-   den!
Thou art dy-   ing.

HILF, HERR JESU, LASS GELINGEN

Christmas Oratorio (B.W. V², p. 166)

Hymn by Johann Rist 1642
Translation by J. Troutbeck

Melody attributed to J.S. Bach 1734

Hymn by Johann Kolross   Melody from Praxis pietatis 1662
Translation by C. Sanford Terry

Cantata 133 Ich freue mich in dir. (B.W. XXVIII, p. 80)

Hymn by Caspar Ziegler 1697   Melody from König's Harmonischer Liederschatz 1738
Translation by Elvera Wonderlich

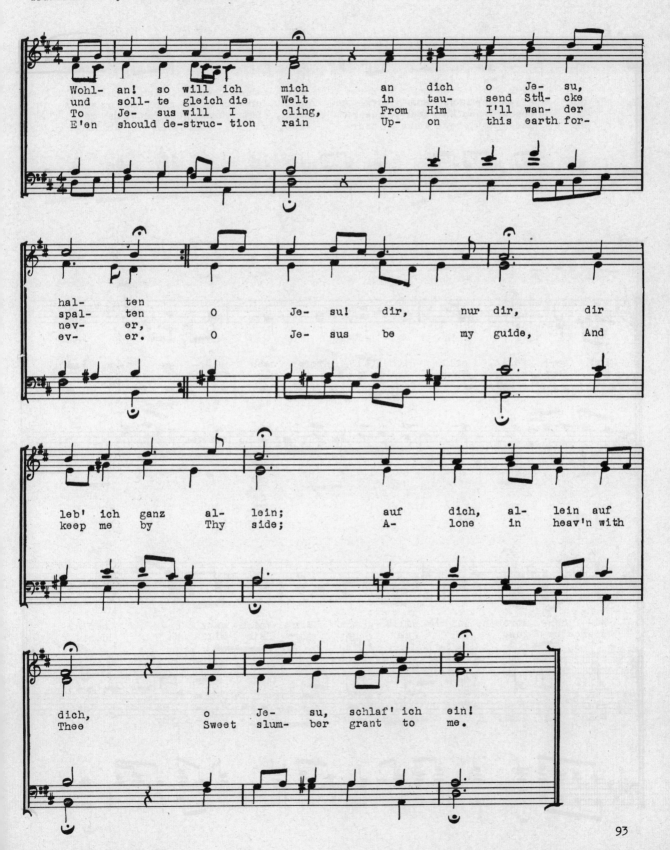

ICH HAB' MEIN SACH GOTT HEIMGESTELLT

(B.W. XXXIX, p. 226)

Hymn by Johannes Leon 1589
Translation by Catherine Winkworth

Melody from Rhau's Gesangbuch 1589

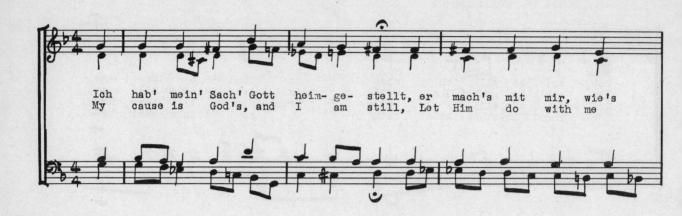

Ich hab' mein' Sach' Gott heim- ge- stellt, er mach's mit mir, wie's
My cause is God's, and I am still, Let Him do with me

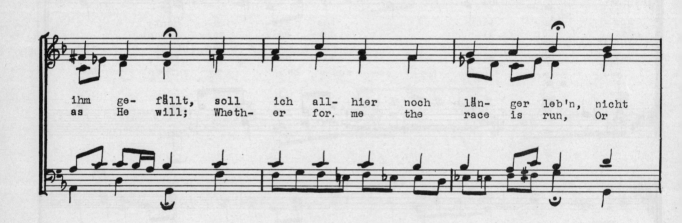

ihm ge- fällt, soll ich all- hier noch län- ger leb'n, nicht
as He will; Wheth- er for- me the race is run, Or

wi- der- streb'n, sei'm Will'n thu' ich mich ganz er- geb'n.
scarce be- gun, I ask no more His will be done!

Hymn by Johann Franck 1655   Melody by Christoph Peter 1655
Translation by Elvera Wonderlich

IN DICH HAB' ICH GEHOFFET HERR

Christmas Oratorio (B.W. V^2, p. 190)

Hymn by Georg Weissel 1642
Translation by J. Troutbeck

Melody from Nürnberger Psalter 1581

St. Matthew Passion (B.W. IV, p. 151)

Hymn by Adam Reissner 1533   Melody from Nürnberger Psalter 1581
Translation by John S. Dwight

Mir   hat die Welt — — trüg-   lich   ge-
The ruth-less world — — ar- raign-   eth

richt't mit Lü-   gen   und mit falsch-em   G'dicht, viel Netz und
me   On false re- port and cal- um-   ny, With many a

heim- lich Strik-   ken. Herr, nimm mein   wahr   in die- ser
toil   to   snare   me.   O   Lord, be   near,   To   stay my

G'fahr, b'hüt mich   vor   fal- — schen   Tük-   ken.
fear; 'Gainst all their arts — pre- pare   me!

Cantata 58 Ich bin ein guter Hirt (B.W. XX^1 p. 118)

Hymn by Christoph Homburg 1659   Melody from Hundert...Arien. Dresden, 1694
Translation by Charles N. Boyd

Ist   Gott mein Schutz und   treu-   er Hirt, kein
With   God my guard and   shep- herd true, Mis-

Un-   glück mich be- rüh-   ren wird; weicht, al-   le   mei- ne
for-   tune can- not me   sub-due; From   foes He will de-

Fein-   de,   die   ihr mir stif- tet Angst und Pein, es
liv-   er.   The grief and pain they   plan for   me Up-

98

wird   zu eu- rem   Scha-   den sein; ich   ha-   be   Gott zum
on   themselves shall turn-   ed be, For   God my   Friend is

Freun-   de, ich   ha-   be   Gott zum   Freun-   de.
ev-   er, For   God my   Friend is   ev-   er.

No. 88   JESU, DER DU MEINE SEELE

(B.W. XXXIX p. 228)

Hymn by Johann Rist 1641   Melody from Praxis Pietatis 1662
Translation by C. Sanford Terry

Je-   su   der du   mei- ne   See-   le   hast durch
aus   des Teu- fels finst- rer   Höh-   le   und der
Je-   su, Who de- liv'- rance brought me   By Thine
In   hell's chains had Sa- tan   bound me   If Thou

dei- nen bit- tern Tod
schwe- ren Sün- den- noth
own most bit- ter woe,
had'st not loved me so.

kräf- tig- lich her-
From the tomb 'tis

aus- ge- ris- sen und mich Sol- ches las- sen
Thou wilt call me, And in heav- en wilt in-

wis- sen durch dein an- ge- neh- mes Wort:
stall me. Through the strength Thy Word doth yield,

sei doch itzt, o Gott, mein Hort.
Be Thou still, dear Lord, my Shield!

St. John Passion (B.W. XII[1] p. 103)

Hymn by Paul Stockmann 1633   Melody from Vulpius' Gesangbuch 1609
Translation by Dr. T.A. Lacey

Er nahm Al- les wohl in Acht   in der letz- ten
See Him now, the Right- eous One,   His last hour a-

Stun- de,   sei- ne Mut- ter,   noch be- dacht',
bid- ing,   For His Mo- ther,   faith- ful Son,

setzt ihr ein'n Vor- mun- de.   O Mensch, ma- che
Faith- ful care pro- vid- ing.   Work, O, man, for

Rich- tig- keit,   Gott   und   Mensch- en   lie-   be,
right- eous- ness,   God   and   man   be-   friend-   ing;

stirb   da- rauf   ohn' al- les Leid,   und dich nicht be-   trü-   be!
Death   shall come   with- out dis- tress,   All dis- qui- et   end-   ing.

No. 90   JESU LEIDEN, PEIN UND TOD

St. John Passion (B.W. XII^{I}, p. 39)

Hymn by Paul Stockmann 1633   Melody from Vulpius' Gesangbuch 1609
Translation by Dr. T. A. Lacey

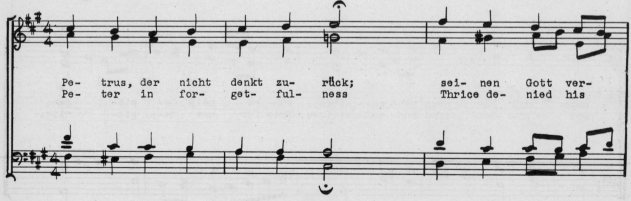

Pe- trus, der nicht denkt zu- rück;   sei- nen   Gott ver-
Pe- ter in for- get- ful- ness   Thrice de- nied his

nei-   **net,**   der   doch   auf   ein'n   ern-   sten   Blick
Mas-   ter;   One   look   moved   him   to   con-   fess,

bit-   ter-   li-   chen   wei-   net: Je-   su,   bli-   cke
Weep-   ing,   his   dis-   as-   ter.   Je-   su,   turn   to

mich   auch   an,   wenn   ich   nicht   will   bü-   -   ssen;
look   on   me,   Who   per- sist   in   sin- .- ning;

wenn   ich   Bö-   ses   hab'   ge-   than,   rüh-   re   mein   Ge-   wis-   sen.
Set   my   fet- tered con-   science free, Free   for new   be-   gin-   ning.

Hymn by Johann Franck 1655
Translation by Catherine Winkworth

Melody by Johann Crüger 1653

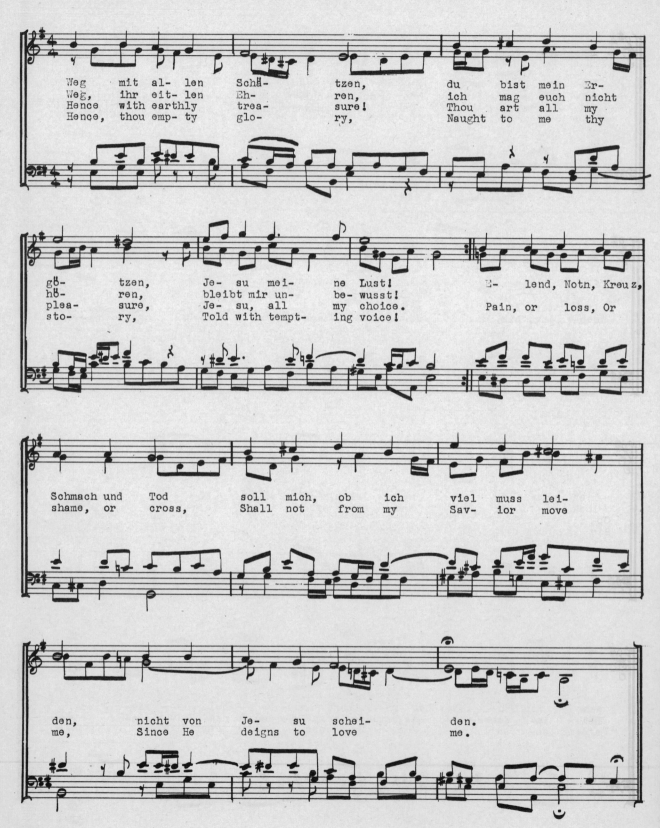

JESU, MEINE FREUDE

Cantata 81 Jesus schläft, was soll ich hoffen? (B.W.XI.[1] p. 24)

Hymn by Johann Franck 1655
Translation by Catherine Winkworth

Melody by Johann Crüger 1653

Un- ter dei- nen Schir- men, bin ich vor den
Lass den Sa- tan wit- tern, lass den Feind er-
In Thine arm I rest me, Foes who would mo-
Though the earth be shak- ing, Ev'- ry heart be

Stür- men, al- ler Fein- de frei
bit- tern, mir steht Je- sus bei.
lest me, Can not reach me here;
quak- ing, Je- sus calms my fear;

Ob es jetzt gleich kracht und blitzt, ob- gleich Sünd und
Sin and hell in con- flict fell With their bit- ter

Höl- le schre- cken: Je- sus will mich de- cken.
storms as- sail me, Je- sus will not fail me.

(B.W. XXXIX, p. 231)

Hymn by Johann Franck 1655
Translation by Catherine Winkworth

Melody by Johann Crüger 1653

Je- su, mei- ne Freu- de, mei- nes Her- zens
ach wie lang', ach lan- ge ist dem Her- zen
Je- su price- less trea- sure, Source of pur- est
Ah! how long I've pant- ed, And my heart hath

Wei- de, Je- su mei- ne Zier,
ban- ge, und ver- langt nach dir.
plea- sure, Tru- est Friend to me;
faint- ed, Thirst- ing Lord, for Thee!

Got- tes Lamm mein Bräu- ti- gam, aus- ser dir soll
Thine I am, O spot- less lamb, I will suf- fer

mir auf Er- den nichts sonst lie- bers wer- den.
nought to hide Thee, Nought I ask be- side Thee.

Motet Jesu, meine Freude (B.W. XXXIX, p. 61-84)

Hymn by Johann Franck 1655
Translation by Catherine Winkworth

Melody by Johann Crüger 1653

Je- su, mei- ne Freu-   de,   mei- nes Her- zens
ach, wie lang', ach Freu- lan- ge   ist dem Her- zen
Je- su price- less trea- sure,   Source of pur- est
Ah! how long I've pant- ed,   And my   heart hath

Wei-   de,   Je-   su,   mei- ne   Zier,
ban-   ge,   und ver- langt nach dir!
plea-   sure   Tru- est Friend to   me;
faint-   ed,   Thirst- ing Lord, for Thee!

Got- tes Lamm, mein Bräu- ti- gam,   au- sser dir soll
Thine I   am,   O   spot- less lamb,   I   will suf- fer

mir   auf Er-   den nichts sonst Lie- bers wer-   den.
nought to hide   Thee, Nought I   ask be- side   Thee.

Cantata 190 Singet dem Herrn ein neues Lied. (B.W. XXXVII, p. 257)

Hymn by Johann Hermann c. 1591
Translation by C. Sanford Terry

Melody from Wittenberg Cantilenae 1591

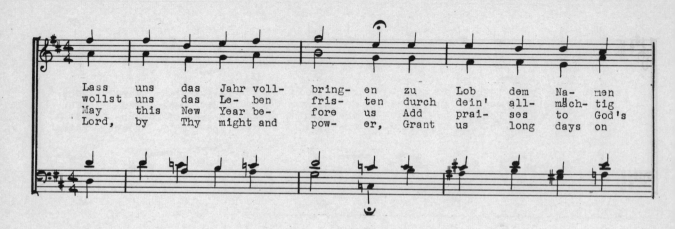

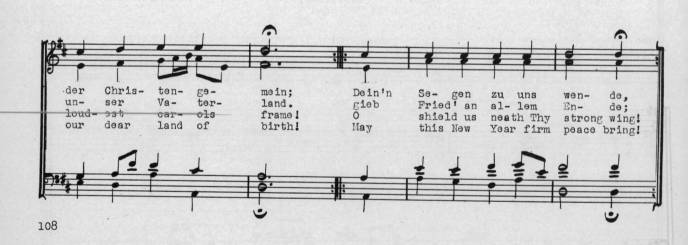

gieb un- ver- fälscht im Lan- de dein se- lig- ma- chend Wort.
Die Heuchler mach' zu Schan- de hier und am al- lem Ort,
Stab- lish a- mong be- liev- ers Thine own Al- migh-ty realm,
And all earth's vain de- ceiv- ers Right ut- ter- ly o'er- whelm!

die Heuch-ler mach' zu Schan- de hier und am al- len Ort.
And all earth's vain de- ceiv- ers Right ut- ter- ly o'er- whelm.

No. 96   JESUS CHRISTUS, UNSER HEILAND

(B.W. XXXIX, p. 234)

Hymn by Martin Luther 1524   Melody from Erfurt Enchiridion 1524
Translation by C.S. Terry

Je- sus Chri-   - stus, un- ser Hei- land,
Christ our Sav-   - iour hath re- deemed us,

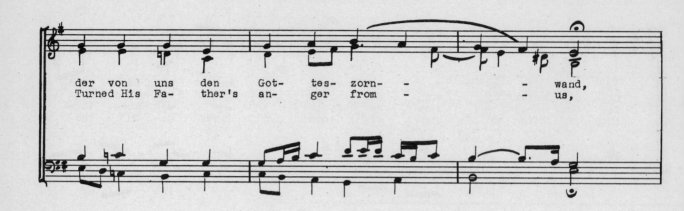

der von uns den Got- tes- zorn - - wand,
Turned His Fa- ther's an- ger from - - us,

durch das bitt- re Lei- - - den sein half
By the bit- ter cross He bore, And

er uns aus der Höl- - - len- pein.
saved us all from Sa- - - tan's power.

110

JESUS, MEINE ZUVERSICHT

(B.W. XXXIX,.p. 235)

Hymn by Luise Henriette of Brandenburg 1653   Melody from Crügers Praxis Pietatis 1653
Translation by Catherine Winkworth

Je— sus, mei— ne Zu— ver— sicht   und   mein Hei— land,
Die— ses weiss ich, soll ich nicht   da—   rum mich zu—
Je— sus Christ, my sure de— fence   And   my Sav— iour
Know— ing this my con— fi— dence   Rests   up— on the

ist im Le—   ben:
frie— den ge—   beth;
ev— er liv—   eth,
hope it giv—   eth,

Was die lan— ge
Though the night of

To— des— nacht   mir auch für Ge— dan— ken macht.
death be fraught   Still with many an anx— ious thought.

Cantata 145 So du mit deinem Munde bekennest Jesum (B.W. XXX, p. 95)

Hymn by Caspar Neumann c. 1700   Melody from Crüger's Praxis Pietatis 1653
Translation by C. Sanford Terry

Auf, mein Herz! Des Her- ren Tag hat die Nacht der
Chri- stus, der im Gra- be lag, ist im To- de
Up, my soul, 'tis God's great day, Death no long- er
He Who in the dark grave lay Ris'n and glo- rious

Furcht ver- trie- ben: Nun- mehr bin ich recht ge- tröst't,
nicht ge- blie- ben. Ev- er will I trust in Him
can en- thral us!
goes be- fore us.

Je- sus hat die Welt er- löst.
Who hath brought the world from sin.

112

KOMM, GOTT SCHÖPFER, HEILIGER GEIST

(B.W. XXXIX, p. 238)

Hymn by Martin Luther 1524
Translation by Dr. Bacon

Melody from Klug's Geistliche Lieder 1535

Komm, Gott Schö- pfer, hei- li- ger Geist, be-
Come, God Cre- a- tor, Ho- ly Ghost, And

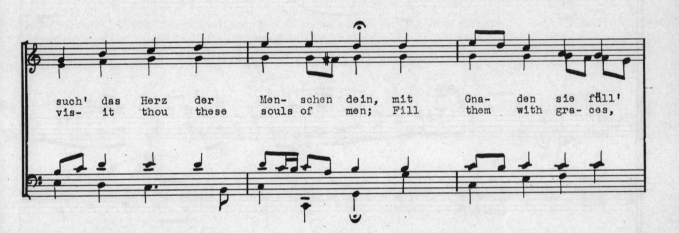

such' das Herz der Men- schen dein, mit Gna- den sie füll'
vis- it thou these souls of men; Fill them with gra- ces,

wie du weisst, dass dein Ge- schöpf soll für dir sein.
as thou dost, Thy cre- tures make pure a- gain.

Cantata 108 Es ist euch gut, dass ich hingehe (B.W. XXIII, p. 230)

Hymn by Paul Gerhardt 1653   Melody from Schumann's Geistliche Lieder 1539
Translation by C. Sanford Terry

Dein Geist, den Gott vom Him- mel giebt, der lei- tet Al- les,
His Spir- it, Whom God sends at need, Us on His right-eous

was ihn liebt, auf wohl ge-bahn- ten We- gen. Er setzt und
paths will lead, Our foot- steps e'er pro- tect- ing. They shall not

rich- tet un- sern Fuss, dass er nicht an- ders tre-ten
wan- der from His ways, Nor be en- snared in Sa-tan's

muss, als wo man find't den Se- gen.
maze, Who fol- low His di- rect- ing.

(B.W. XXXIX, p. 240)

Hymn by Tobias Clausnitzer 1663   Melody from Ahle's Sonntagsandachten 1664
Translation by Catherine Winkworth

Lieb-	ster	Je-	su		wir	sind	hier,		dich	und	dein Wort
len-	ke	Sin-	nen		und	Be-	gier		auf	die	sü- ssen
Bles-	sed	Je-	su,		at	Thy	word		We	are	gath-ered
Let	our	hearts and		souls	be	stirred		Now	to	seek and

an-	zu-	hö-		ren;	dass	die	Her-	zen
Him-	mels-	leh-		ren,				
all	to	hear		Thee;	By	Thy	teach-	ings
love	and	fear		Thee,				

| von | der | Er- | den | ganz | zu | dir | ge- | zo- | gen wer- | den. |
| sweet | and | ho- | ly | Drawn | from earth to | | | love Thee sole- | ly. |

LOBT GOTT, IHR CHRISTEN, ALLZUGLEICH

(B.W. XXXIX, p. 241)

Hymn by Nicolaus Herman c. 1554
Translation by August Crill

Melody by Nicolaus Herman 1554

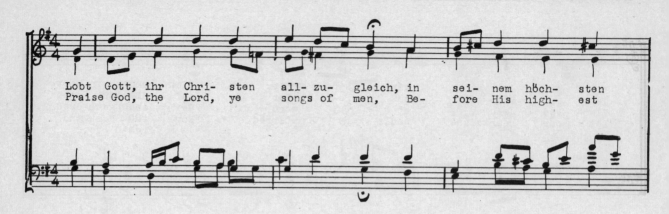

Lobt Gott, ihr Chri- sten all- zu- gleich, in sei- nem höch- sten
Praise God, the Lord, ye songs of men, Be- fore His high- est

Thron; der heut' auf- schleusst sein Him- mel- reich und
Throne, To- day He o- pens heav'n a- gain, And

schenkt uns sei- nen Sohn, — und schenkt uns sei- nen Sohn.
gives us His Own Son, — And gives us His Own Son.

MACH'S MIT MIR, GOTT, NACH DEINER GÜT'

(B.W. XXXIX, p. 242)

Hymn by Johann Schein 1628
Translation by Catherine Winkworth

Melody by Johann Schein 1628

Mach's mit mir, Gott, nach dei- ner Güt', hilf
was ich dich bitt', ver- sag' mir nicht, wenn
Deal with me, God, in mer- cy now, Oh
Thine ear to me in pi- ty bow; When

mir in mei- nem Lei- den, so nimm sie, Herr, in
mei- ne Seel' will schei- den; Re- ceive her, as her-
help me in my utter woe
hence my soul must quickly go,

dei- ne Händ', ist Al- les gut, wenn gut das End'.
God and Friend, For all is right if right the end.

Cantata 10 Meine Seel' erhebt den Herren (B.W. I, p. 303)

Hymn by Gloria Patri
Translation anonymous

Melody Tonus peregrinus

Lob und Preis sei Gott dem Va- ter und dem
Glo- ry be to God the Fa- ther and the

Sohn und dem hei- li- gen Gei- -
Son, and to the Ho- ly Ghost -

ste, wie es war im An- fang jetzt und
As it was in the be- gin-

im- mer- dar und von E- wig- keit zu
ning is now and shall be ev- er-

E— wig- keit, A— — men.
more. A— — men.

No. 105   MEINE SEELE ERHEBT DEN HERREN

(B.W. XXXIX, p. 212)

Hymn Benediction   Melody Tonus peregrinus
Translation anonymous

Gott —   sei uns gnä- dig und barm—
The —   Lord for ev- er bless and

her-   zig   und -
keep   us,   and

geb' uns sei- nen   gött-   li-   chen   Se- -
ev- er- more give   us   His   bless- -

gen.
ing.

Cantata 70 Wachet betet seid bereit (B.W. XVI, p. 368)

Hymn by Christian Keimann 1658   Melody from Hammerschmiedt's Fest, Bus und
Translation by C. Sanford Terry   Danck Lieder 1658

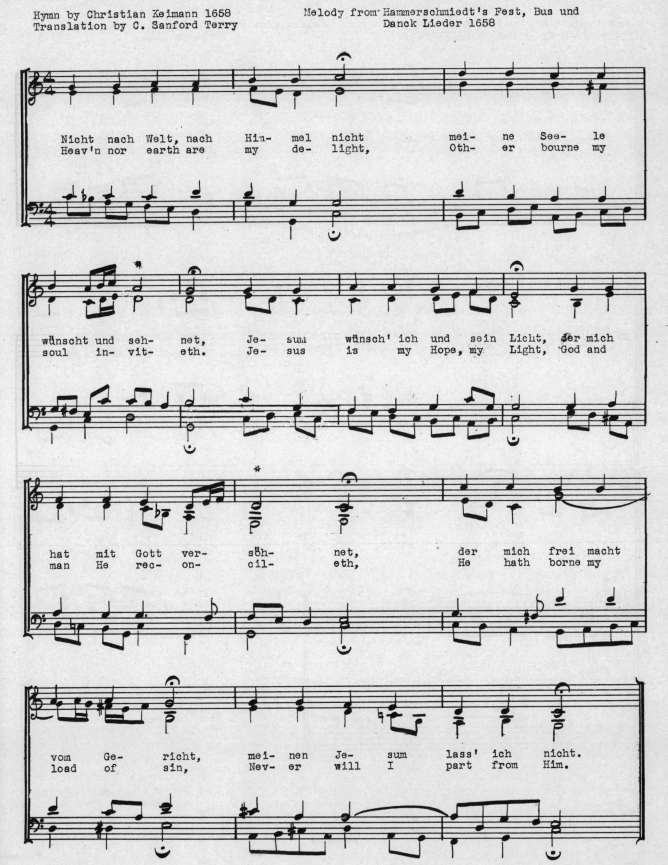

Nicht nach Welt, nach   Him- mel nicht   mei- ne See- le
Heav'n nor earth are   my de- light,   Oth- er bourne my

wünscht und seh- net,   Je- sum wünsch' ich und sein Licht, der mich
soul in- vit- eth.   Je- sus is my Hope, my Light, God and

hat mit Gott ver- söh- net,   der mich frei macht
man He rec- on- cil- eth,   He hath borne my

vom Ge- richt,   mei- nen Je- sum lass' ich nicht.
load of sin,   Nev- er will I part from Him.

* Chord third appears in instrumental accompaniment.

MIT FRIED' UND FREUD' ICH FAHR DAHIN

(B.W. XXXIX, p. 245)

Hymn by Martin Luther 1524
Translation by Catherine Winkworth

Melody from Walter's Geystliche gesangk
Buchleyn 1524

Mit Fried' und Freud' ich fahr' da- hin in Got- tes Wil-
In peace and joy I now de- part, Ac- cord- ing to God's

le, ge- trost ist mir mein Herz und Sinn, sanft-
will, For full of com- fort is my heart, So

- und stil - le. Wie Gott mir ver- hei- ssen
calm and sweet and still; So doth God His pro- mise

hat, der Tod ist mein Schlaf wor- den.
keep, And death to me is but a sleep.

Hymn by Martin Luther 1524   Melody from Walter's Geystliche gesangk Buchleyn 1524
Translation by Catherine Winkworth

Er   ist   das   Heil   und   se-   lig   Licht   für   -   die   Hei-
He   is   the   hea-   then's   sa-   ving   light,   And   He   will   gent-ly

den,   zu er-   leuch-   ten,   die   dich   ken-   -   -   nen
lead   Those   who   now   know   Thee   not   -   -   a-

nicht,   und   zu   wei-   den.   Er   ist   dein's   Volks
right   And   in   His   pastures   feed: While   His   peo-   ples'

I-   sra-   el   der   Preis,   Ehr,   Freud'   und   Won-   ne.
joy   He   is,   Their   Sun,   their   Glo-   ry,   and   their   bliss.

NICHT SO TRAURIG, NICHT SO SEHR

(B.W. XXXIX, p. 247)

Hymn by Paul Gerhardt 1648
Translation by Mrs. Eric Findlater

Melody attributed to J.S. Bach 1736

Nicht so trau-rig, nicht so sehr, mei-ne
dass dir Gott Glück, Gut und Ehr' nicht so
Ah! grieve not so, nor so la-ers ment, My --
Be-cause some joys to oth-ers sent Thy --

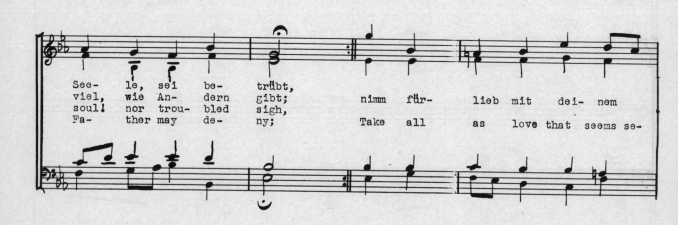

See-le, sei be-trübt,
viel, wie An-dern gibt; nimm für lieb mit dei-nem
soul! nor trou-bled sigh,
Fa-ther may de-ny; Take all as love that seems se-

Gott; hast du Gott, so hat's nicht Noth.
vere There is no want if God is near.

Cantata 197 Gott ist uns're Zuversicht (B.W. XIII[1], p. 128)

Hymn by Martin Luther 1524   Melody from Walter's Geystliche gesangk Buchleyn 1524
Translation by A.T. Russell

Du sü- sse Lieb', schenk'- uns dei- ne Gunst, lass
Spir- it of love, now - our spir-its bless; Them

uns em- pfin - den der Lie- be Brunst, dass wir
with thy own - heaven-ly fire pos- sess; That in

uns von Her- zen ein an der lie-   ben,
heart u- nit- ing, In peace de- light-   ing,

und in Fried' auf ei- nem Sin- ne blei- ben.
We may hence- forth all be one in spir- it.

Ky- ri- e e- leis!
Have mer- cy, Lord.

No. 111   NUN DANKET ALLE GOTT

(B.W. XXXIX, p. 248)

Hymn by Martin Rinkart 1648   Melody by Johann Crüger 1648
Translation by Catherine Winkworth

Nun dan- ket al- le Gott mit Her- zen, Mund und
der gros- se Din- ge thut an uns und al- len
Now thank we all our God, With heart and hands and
Who won- drous things hath done, In whom His world re-

Hän- den, der uns von Mut- ter- leib und
En- voi- ces, Who from our mo- thers' arms Hath
joi- ces;

Kin- des- bei- nen an un- zäh- lig viel zu
bless'd u on our way With count- less gifts of

gut und noch jetz und ge- than.
love, And still is ours to- day.

NUN DANKET ALLE GOTT
Trauungschoral (B.W. XIII[1], p. 149)

Hymn by Martin Rinkart 1648
Translation by Catherine Winkworth

Melody by Johann Crüger 1648

NUN FREUT EUCH, GOTTES KINDER ALL'

(B.W. XXXIX p. 248)

Hymn by Erasmus Alber c. 1549
Translation by Elvera Wonderlich

Melody from a broadsheet c. 1546

Nun freut euch, Got- tes Kin- der all, der
O chil- dren of your God, re- joice, To

Herr fährt auf mit gro- ssem Schall, lob- sin- get ihm lob-
Him lift up both heart and voice. Praise ye the Lord, praise

sin- get ihm, lob- sin- get ihm mit hel- ler Stimm'!
ye the Lord, Sing praise to Him with one ac- cord.

Cantata 36 Schwingt freudig euch empor (B.W. VII, p. 258)

Hymn by Martin Luther 1524   Melody from Erfurt Enchiridion 1524
Translation by Richard Massie

Lob sei Gott dem Va- ter g'than,   Lob sei Gott sein'm
Praise be to the Fa- ther done,   Praise be to the

ein'- gen Sohn,   Lob sei Gott dem heil'- gen Geist
on- ly Son,   Prai- ses to the Spir- it be,

im- mer und in E- wig- keit.
Now and to e- ter- ni- ty.

130

Cantata 194 Höchsterwünschstes Freudenfest (B.G. XXIX, p. 138)

Hymn by Paul Gerhardt 1647   Melody by Nikolaus Selnecker 1587
Translation by H.J. Buckoll

Sprich Ja zu mei- nen Tha- ten, hilf selbst das Be- ste ra- then; den An- fang, Mitt'l und En- de, ach Herr, zum Be- sten wen- - - de.

Mit Se- gen mich be- schüt- te, mein Herz sei dei- ne Hüt- te, dein Wort sei mei- ne Spei- se, bis ich gen Him- mel rei- - - se.

Thou all I do pro- tect- ing, And ev'- ry thought di- rect- ing, First, Thy last, Be- gin- ning, end- ing, Let all to Good be tend- - - ing.

Lord, pour Thy spir- it's bless- ing, This heart Thy home pos- sess- ing; Thy Word my food be giv- en, Till hence I soar to heav- - - en!

Hymn by Johann Graumann 1540   Melody by Johann Kugelmann 1540
Translation by Catherine Winkworth

Wie sich ein Vat'r er- bar- met üb'r
So thut der Herr uns Ar- - men, so
For as a ten- der fa- - ther Hath
He in his arms will ga- - ther All

sei- ne jun- ge Kind- lein klein:
wir ihn kind- lich ge fürch- ten rein.
pi- ty on His chil- dren here,
who are His in child- like fear.

Er kennt das arm Ge- mäch- te, er
He knows how frail our pow- ers, Who

weiss, wir sind nur Staub. Gleich wie das
but from dust are made: We flour- ish

Gras vom Re- - che, ein' Blum' und
as the flow- - ers, And ev- en

fal- lend Laub. der Wind nur drü- ber
so we fade. A storm wind o'er them

we- het, so ist es nim- mer
pass- es, And all their bloom is

da; al- so der Mensch ver- ge -
o'er; We wi- ther like the grass- -

het,   sein   End',   das   ist -   ihm   nah.
es,   Our   place   knows   us   no   more.

No. 117   NUN SICH DER TAG GEENDET HAT

(B.W. XXXIX, p. 252)

Hymn by Johann Hertzog 1670   Melody from Krieger's Neue Arien 1667
Translation by Catherine Winkworth

Nun   sich   der   Tag ge-   en-   det hat,   und   kei- ne   Sonn' mehr scheint, schläft
Now   that   the   sun doth   shine   no more,   And   day hath reach'd its close, They

Al-   les,   was   sich   ab- ge-   matt', und   was   zu- vor   ge- weint.
calm- ly   sleep who   wept be- fore, The   wea- ried find   re- pose.

O EWIGKEIT, DU DONNERWORT

Cantata 20 O Ewigkeit, du Donnerwort (B.W. II, p. 327)

Hymn by Johann Rist 1642
Translation by J.C. Jacobi

Melody from Crügers Praxis pietatis 1653

O E- wig- keit, du Don- ner- wort, o
E- ter- ni- ty, tre- men- dous word, Home-

Schwert, das durch die See- le bohrt, o An- fang son- der
strik- ing point, heart- pierc- ing sword, Be- gin- ning with- out

En- de!
end- ing!

Nimm du mich, wenn es dir ge- fällt, Herr
Lord Je- su, when it pleas- es Thee, Bring

Je- su, in dein Freu- den- zelt.
me to blest e- ter- ni- ty.

Cantata 45 Es ist dir gesagt, Mensch, was gut ist (B.W. X p. 186)

Hymn by Johann Heermann 1630   Melody from Fritsch's Himmels-Lust und
Translation by Catherine Winkworth   Welt-Unlust 1679

Gieb,   dass   ich thu' mit Fleiss,   was   mir   zu   thun ge-
And   grant me, Lord, to   do,   With   read-   y   heart and

büh-   ret, wo-   zu   mich dein Be-   fehl   in
will-   ing, What- e'er Thou shalt com-   mand,   My

mei-   nem Stan- de füh-   ret. Gieb,   dass ich's thu e
call-   ing here ful- fill-   ing, And   do   it   when I

bald,   Zu   der   Zeit, da ich   soll;   und

ought,   With   all   my strength; and bless   the

wenn ich's thu', so   gieb,   dass   es   ge- ra- the wohl.

work   I   thus have wrought,   For   Thou must give suc- cess.

No. 120   O GOTT, DU FROMMER GOTT

Cantata 24 Ein ungefärbt Gemüthe (B.W. V^I, p. 150)

Hymn by Johann Heermann 1630   Melody from Meiningishes Gesangbuch 1693
Translation by Catherine Winkworth

O   Gott, du   from- mer Gott,   du Brunn- quell

O   God, Thou faith- ful God,   Thou Foun- tain

al— ler Ga— ben, ohn' den nichts ist, was ist, von
ev— er flow— ing, With— out whom no— thing is, All

dem wir Al— les ha— ben: ge— sun— den Leib gieb
per— fect gifts be— stow— ing; A pure and heal— thy

mir, und dass in sol— chem Leib ein' un— ver— letz— te
frame O give me, and with— in A con— science free from

Seel' und rein Ge— wis— sen bleib!
blame, A soul un— hurt by sin.

Cantata 46 Schauet doch und sehet, ob irgend ein Schmerz sei (B.W. X, p. 236)

Hymn by Balthasar Schnurr 1632   Melody attributed to Melchior Franck 1632
Translation by C. Sanford Terry

O   gro- sser Gott der   Treu', weil   vor   dir   Nie- mand gilt als
O   Lord, Thou God of   Truth, Be-   fore Whom   none may   stand If

dein Sohn Je- sus   Christ,   der   dei-   nen Zorn ge-
Je-   sus   Christ Thy   Son   Stay   not   Thy wrath- ful

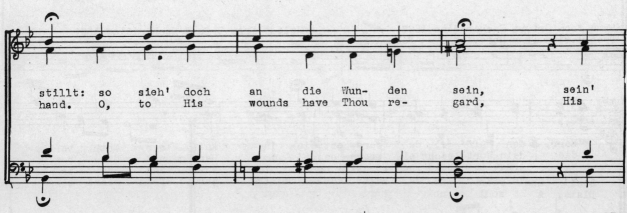

stillt: so sieh' doch   an   die Wun- den   sein,   sein'
hand. 0,   to   His   wounds have Thou re-   gard,   His

Mar- ter, Angst und schwe- re Pein. Um sei- net- wil- len
an- guish, pain, and bo- dy marred: For His dear sake, O

scho- ne, und nicht nach Sün- den loh- ne.
spare us, And on Thy mer- cy bear us!

No. 122   O HERRE GOTT, DEIN GÖTTLICH WORT

Cantata 184 Erwünschtes Freudenlicht (B.W. XXXVII, p. 95)

Hymn from Erfurt Enchiridion 1527   Melody from Erfurt Enchiridion 1527
Translation from Moravian Hymn Book 1754

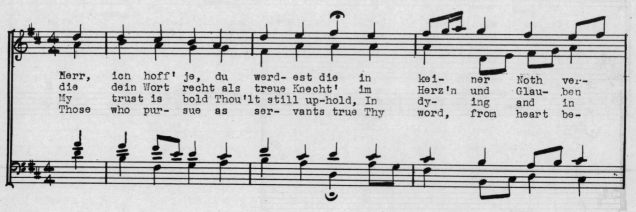

Herr, ich hoff' je, du werd- est die in kei- ner Noth ver-
die dein Wort recht als treue Knecht' im Herz'n und Glau- ben
My trust is bold Thou'lt still up-hold, In dy- ing and in
Those who pur- sue as ser- vants true Thy word, from heart be-

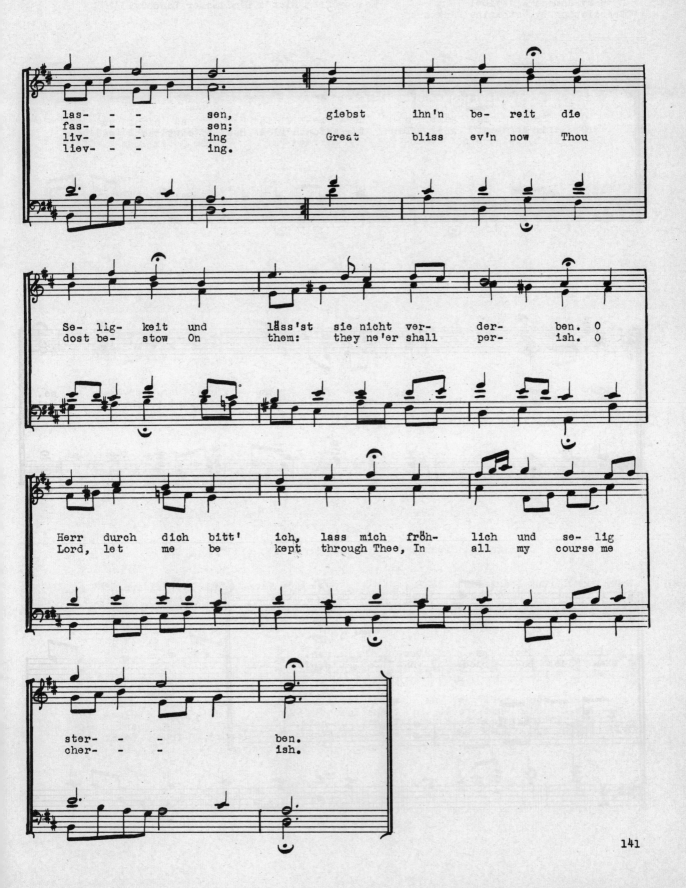

las- - - sen, giebst ihn'n be- reit die
fas- - - sen;
liv- - - ing Great bliss ev'n now Thou
liev- - - ing.

Se- lig- keit und läss'st sie nicht ver- der- ben. O
dost be- stow On them: they ne'er shall per- ish. O

Herr durch dich bitt' ich, lass mich fröh- lich und se- lig
Lord, let me be kept through Thee, In all my course me

ster- - - ben.
cher- - - ish.

O TRAURIGKEIT, O HERZELEID

(B.W. XXXIX, p. 257)

Hymn by Johann Rist 1641
Translation by Catherine Winkworth

Melody from Rist's Himlischer Lieder 1641

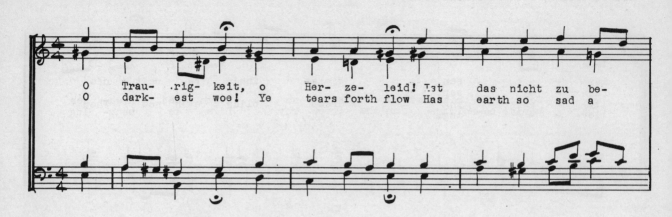

O Trau- .rig- keit, o Her- ze- leid! Ist das nicht zu be-
O dark- est woe! Ye tears forth flow Has earth so sad a

kla- gen? Got- tes Va- ters ei- nigs Kind
won- der, That the fa- ther's on- ly Son

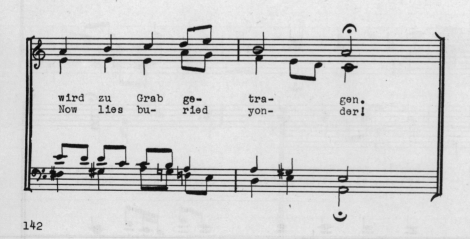

wird zu Grab ge- tra- gen.
Now lies bu- ried yon- der!

No. 124   O WELT, ICH MUSS DICH LASSEN

(B.W. XXXIX, p. 251)

Hymn by Paul Gerhardt 1648
Translation by Catherine Winkworth

Melody by Heinrich Isaac c. 1510

O   Welt, sieh' hier dein Le-   ben   am   Stamm des   Kreu- zes
Oh,   world! be-hold up- on the tree Thy   Life   is   hang- ing

schwe- ben,   dein Heil sinkt in   den   Tod,   der
now for   thee, Thy Sav- iour yields His dying   breath;   The

gros- se Fürst der Eh-   ren   lässt   wil- lig sich be-
might- y Prince of glory now For   thee doth un- re-

schwe- ren mit Schlä- ten, Hohn und   gros- sem Spott.
sisting bow To cru- el stripes, To   scorn and death.

143

O WELT ICH MUSS DICH LASSEN

.St. Matthew Passion.(B.W. IV, p. 164)

Hymn by Paul Gerhardt 1648
Translation by J. Troutbeck

Melody by Heinrich Isaac c. 1510

Wer hat dich so ge- schla- gen, mein Heil, und' dich mit
O Lord, who dares to smite Thee, And false-ly to in-

Pla- gen so ü- bel zu- ge- richt? Du
dict Thee, De- ride and mock Thee so? Thou

bist ja nicht ein Sün- der, wie wir und un- sre
canst not need con- fes- sion, Who know- est not trans-

Kin- der; von Mis- se- tha- ten weisst du nicht.
gres- sion, As we and all our chil- dren know.

O WELT, ICH MUSS DICH LASSEN

St. John Passion (B.W. XII, p. 31)

Hymn by Paul Gerhardt 1648
Translation by J. Troutbeck

Melody by Heinrich Isaac c. 1510

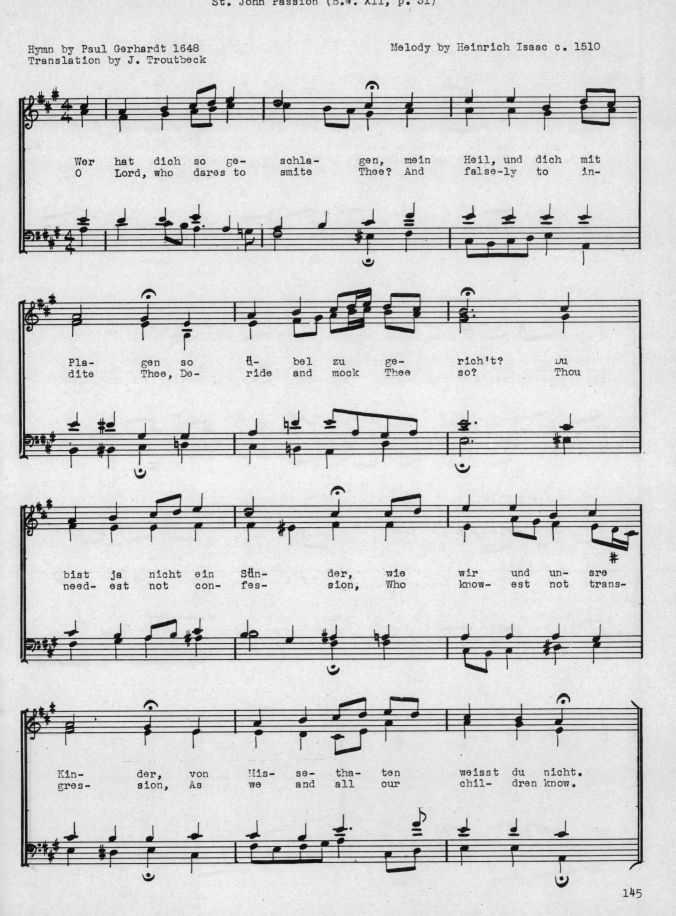

(B.W. XXXIX, p. 258)

Hymn by Simon Dach 1635   Melody from Gesangbuch der Böhmischen Brüder 1566
Translation by Catherine Winkworth

Cantata 65 Sie werden aus Saba Alle kommen (B.W. XVI, p. 152)

Hymn adapted from 14th century Latin hymn   Melody from Lossius' Psalmodia 1553
Translation by H.M. MacGill

Die Kön'-ge aus Sa- ba ka - men dar,
And king- ly pil- grims, long fore- told,

ka - le- lu- men dar, Gold, Weih- rauch
Al- le- lu- - ja. From east bring

Myrr- hen brach- ten sie dar, Al- le- lu-
in- cense, myrrh, and gold. Al- le- lu-

ja, Al- le- - - lu- ja!
ja, Al- le- - - lu- ja!

Cantata 180 Schmücke dich, o liebe Seele (B.W. XXXV, p. 322)

Hymn by Johann Franck 1649
Translation by Catherine Winkworth

Melody by Johann Crüger 1649

Je- su wah- res Brod des Le- leicht zum Scha- bens, hilf, dass
o- der mir viel- leicht zum Scha- den sei zu
Je- sus, Bread of Life, I pray Thee, Let me
Nev- er to my hurt in- vit- ed,, Be Thy

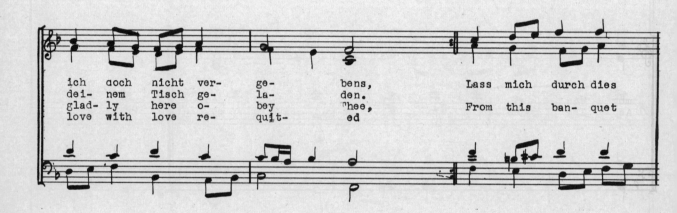

ich doch nicht ver- ge- bens, Lass mich durch dies
dei- nem Tisch ge- la- den. From this ban- quet
glad- ly here o- bey Thee,
love with love re- quit- ed

See- len- Es- sen, dei- ne Lie- be recht er- its
let me mea- sure, Lord how vast and deep
Seel

148

mes-   sen,   dass ich auch, wie   jetzt auf Er- en,
trea-   sure;   Through the gifts Thou   here dost give me

mög ein Gast im Him- mel wer-   ceive   den.
As Thy guest in heav- en re-   ceive   me.

No. 130   SCHWING' DICH AUF ZU DEINEM GOTT

Cantata 40 Dazu ist erschienen der Sohn Gottes (B.W. VII, p. 387)

Hymn by Paul Gerhardt 1653   Melody revised by J.S. Bach 1769
Translation by Albert Riemenschneider

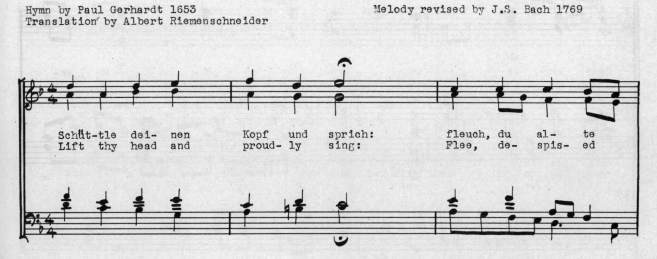

Schüt-tle dei nen Kopf und sprich: fleuch, du al- te
Lift thy head and proud-ly sing: Flee, de- spis- ed

Schlan- ge! was er- neurst du dei- nen Stich,
ser- pent! Why re- new'st thy dead- ly sting,

machst mir angst und ban- ge? Ist dir doch der
Caus- ing fear and tor- ment? Christ in- deed hath

Kopf zer- knickt, und ich bin durch's Lei- de n
bruised thy head, And me, through His sad- ness,

mei- nes Hei- lands dir ent- rückt in den Saal der Freu- den.
From thee to Him- self hath led In the realms of glad- ness.

Cantata 187 Es wartet Alles auf dich (B.W. XXXVII, p. 191)

Hymn anonymous 16th century   Melody from Gesangbuch der Brüder inn Behemen und
Translation by C. Sanford Terry   Merherrn, 1544

Gott   hat die   Erd'   schön   zu- ge-   richt't,
Wir dan-ken sehr   und   bit- ten   ihn,
Well hath our God   the   world or-   dained!
Now thank we Him   and   praise Him   too

lässt's an   Nah-   rung   man- geln   nicht;
dass   er   uns geb!   des   Gei- stes   Sinn,
Good   things on   us   He hath   rained;
Who   doth   our dull   sense re-   new,

Berg   und   Thal,   die   macht er   nass,
dass   wir   sol-   ches   recht ver-   steh'n,
His   the   val-   leys   and the   hills,
Mak-   eth   us   to   grow in   grace

dass   dem   Vieh auch   wächst   sein   Gras;
stets   nach sein'n Ge-   bo-   ten   geh'n,
Herbs   and   pas- ture-   feed-   ing   rills,
And   t'ward His   law   set   our   face.

aus	der	Er —	den	Wein	und	Brod
sei-	nen	Na-	men	ma-	chen	gross
His	the	au-	tumn's	har-	vest	sheaves.
His	name	come	now,	glo-	ri-	fy,

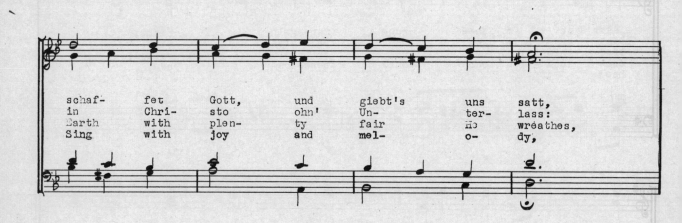

schaf-	fet	Gott,	und	giebt's	uns	satt,
in	Chri-	sto	ohn'	Un-	ter-	lass:
Earth	with	plen-	ty	fair	no	wreathes,
Sing	with	joy	and	mel-	o-	dy,

dass	der	Mensch	sein	Le-	ben	hat.
so	sing'n	wir	das	Gra-	ti-	as.
Life	in-	to	our	be-	ing	breathes.
Gra-	ti-	as	to	God	on	high!

Cantata 115 Mache dich, mein Geist, bereit (B.W. XXIV, p. 132)

Hymn by Johann Freystein 1697   Melody from Hundert ahnmutig und sonderbar geistlicher
Translation by C.S. Terry   Arien 1694

VALET WILL ICH DIR GEBEN

(B.W. XXXIX p. 263)

Hymn by Valerius Herberger 1614
Translation by Catherine Winkworth

Melody by Melchior Teschner 1613

Va-   let will ich dir   ge-   ben, du   ar-   ge   fa-   sche
dein   sünd-lich bö- ses   Le-   ben durch   aus   mir nicht ge-
Fare- well I   glad-ly   bid   Thee, False   e-   vil world fare-
Thy   life is   dark and   sin-   ful, With   thee I   would not

Welt,   Im   Him- mel ist gut woh-   nen, hin-
fällt.   In   heav'n are joys un- troub-   led, I
well!
dwell:

auf steht mein Be- gier,   da   wird Gott e-   wig
long for   that bright sphere Where   God re- wards them

loh-   nen dem, der   ihm dient all-   hier.
dou-   bled Who serv'd Him tru- ly   here.

The bass is A in the Bach Gesellschaft Edition

VALET WILL ICH DIR GEBEN

St. John Passion (B.W. XII^{I}, p. 95)

Hymn by Valerius Herberger 1614
Translation by J. Troutbeck

Melody by Melchior Teschner 1613

In mei- nes Her-zens Grun- de, dein Nam' und Kreuz al-
Fun- kelt all- zeit und Stun- de, drauf kann ich fröh- lich
With- in our in-most be- ing Thy Name and cross a-
The light of all our see- ing, Pre- vail- ing in- fluence

lein
sein. Er- schein' mir in dem Bil- de zu
lone, O breathe this com-fort o'er us, When
own.

Trost in mei- ner Noth, wie du, Herr Christ, so
low in grief we lie, That Thou, Lord Je- sus

mil- de dich hast ge- blut't zu Tod.
for us Hast giv'n Thy- self to die.

VATER UNSER IM HIMMELREICH

Cantata 90 Es reifet euch ein schrecklich Ende (B.W. XX^1, p. 214)

Hymn translated from Latin by Martin Moller 1584
Translation by Elvera Wonderlich

Melody from Schumann's
Geistliche Lieder 1539

Leit' uns mit dei- ner rech- ten Hand, und seg- ne un- ser'
Oh guide us Lord with Thy right hand, And bless and save our

Stadt und Land: gieb uns all- zeit dein heil- ges Wort, be-
fa- ther- land: Pro- tect us with Thy Ho- ly Word, From

hüt' vor Teu- fel's List und Mord, ver- leih' ein sel'- ges
Sa- tan's lure re- move us, Lord, And grant us ho- ly

Stün- de- lein, auf dass wir e- wig bei dir sein!
peace at last With Thee in heav'n when life is past.

Hymn by Martin Luther 1539   Melody from Schumann's Geistliche Lieder 1539
Translation by J. Troutbeck

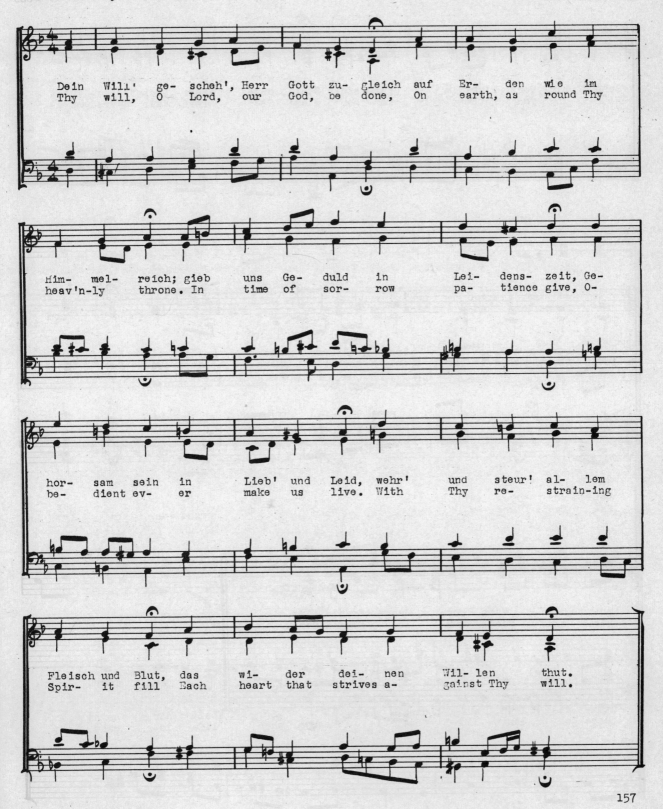

Dein Will' ge- scheh', Herr Gott zu- gleich auf Er- den wie im
Thy will, O Lord, our God, be done, On earth, as round Thy

Him- mel- reich; gieb uns Ge- duld in Lei- dens- zeit, Ge-
heav'n-ly throne. In time of sor- row pa- tience give, O-

hor- sam sein in Lieb' und Leid, wehr' und steur! al- lem
be- dient ev- er make us live. With Thy re- strain-ing

Fleisch und Blut, das wi- der dei- nen Wil- len thut.
Spir- it fill Each heart that strives a- gainst Thy will.

Hymn by Paul Gerhardt 1667   Melody from Schumann's Geistliche Lieder 1539
Translation by J. Troutbeck

Schaut hin! dort liegt im fin-stern Stall, dess' Herr-schaft ge-het
With-in yon gloom-y man-ger lies The Lord who reigns a-

ü-ber all. Da Spei-se vor-mals sucht' ein Rind, da
bove the skies. With-in the stall where beasts have fed The

ru-het jetzt der Jung-frau'n Kind.
Vir-gin born doth lay His head.

Cantata 73 Herr, wie du willst (B.W. XVIII, p. 104)

Hymn by Ludwig Helmbold 1563   Melody from Magdeburg's Christliche und
Translation by Catherine Winkworth   Tröstliche Tischgesenge 1571

Das ist des Va- ters Wil- le, der uns er- schaf- fen
For such His will who made us, The Fa- ther seeks our

hat; sein Sohn hat Gut's die Fül- le er-
good; The Son hath grace to aid us, And

wor- ben uns aus Gnad'; auch Gott, der heil'- ge
save us by His blood; His Spi- rit rules our

159

Geist, im Glau- ben uns re- gie- ret, zum
ways, By faith in us a- bid- ing, To

Reich des Him- mels füh- ret: ihm sei Lob, Ehr' und
heav'n our foot- steps guid- ing; To Him be thanks and

Preis.
praise.

Cantata 140 Wachet auf, ruft uns die Stimme (B.W. XXVIII, p. 284)

Hymn by Philipp Nicolai 1599
Translation by Catherine Winkworth

Melody by Philipp Nicolai 1599

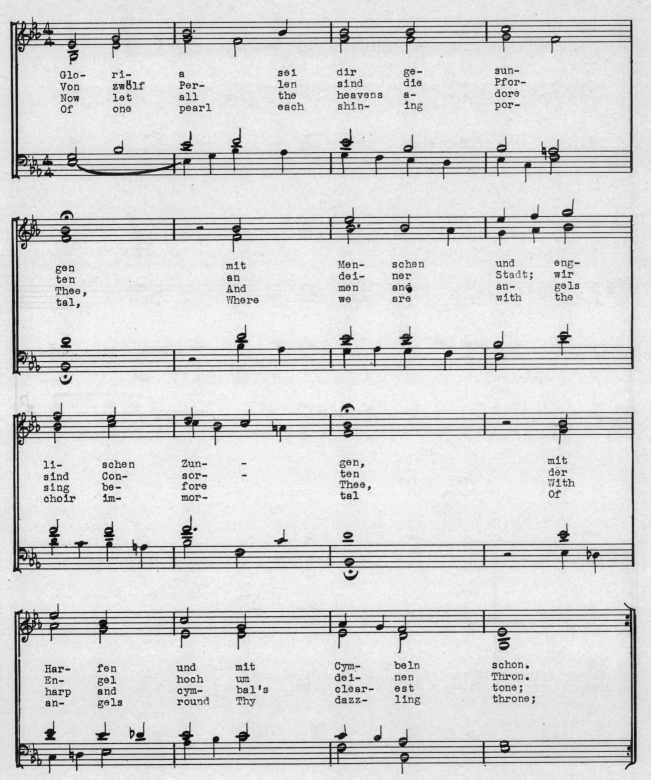

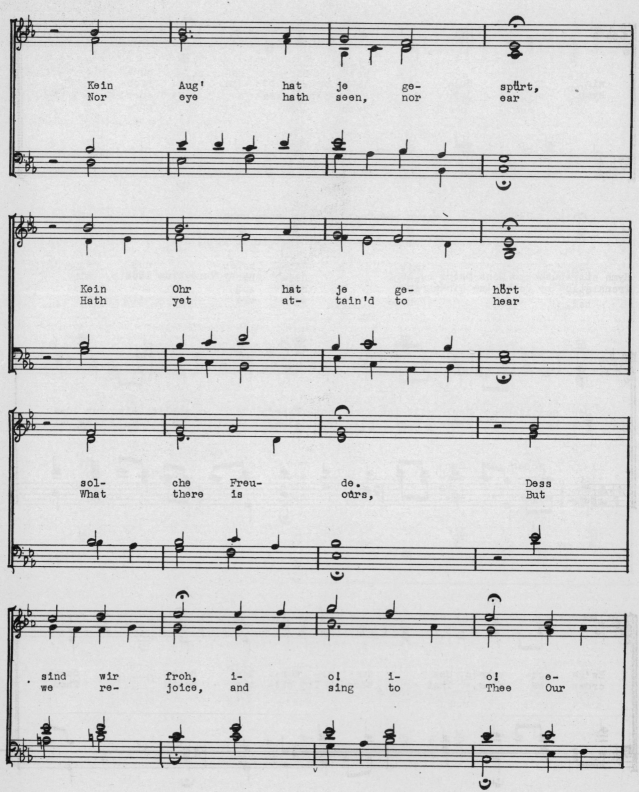

wig   in   dul- ci   ju-   bi-   lo.
hymn   of   joy   e- ter-   nal-   ly.

No. 140   WARUM BETRÜBST DU DICH, MEIN HERZ

Cantata 47 Wer sich selbst erhöhet (B.W. X, p. 274)

Hymn attributed to Hans Sachs c. 1560   Melody by Monoetius 1565
Translation by Catherine Winkworth

Der zeitlichen Ehr' will ich gern ent- behr'n, du   woll'st mir nur das
What here may shine I all re- sign, If   the   e- ter- nal

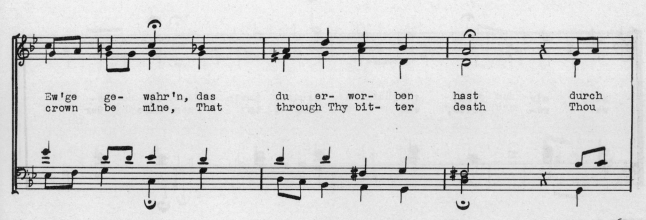

Ew'ge ge- wahr'n, das   du er- wor- ben hast   durch
crown be mine, That through Thy bit- ter death   Thou

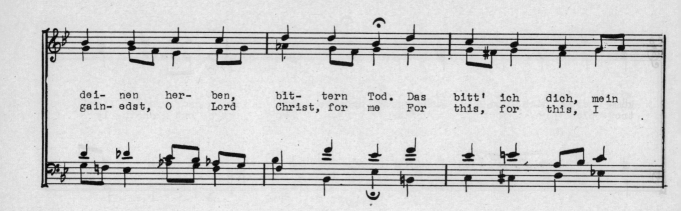

dei- nen her- ben, bit- tern Tod. Das bitt' ich dich, mein
gain- edst, O Lord Christ, for me For this, for this, I

Herr und Gott!
cry to Thee!

No. 141   WARUM BETRÜBST DU DICH, MEIN HERZ

(B.W. XXXIX, p. 266)

Hymn attributed to Hans Sachs c. 1560   Melody by Monoetius 1565
Translation by Catherine Winkworth

Wa- rum be- trübst du dich, mein Herz, be-
Why art thou thus cast down, my heart? Why

kům- merst dich und trä- gest Schmerz nur um das zeit-lich'
trou- bled, why dost mourn a- part, O'er nought but earth-ly

Gut? Ver- trau' du dei- nem Her- ren Gott, der
wealth? Trust in thy God, be not a- fraid, He

al- le Ding' er- schaf- fen hat.
is thy Friend who all things made.

　　　　WARUM SOLLT' ICH MICH DENN GRÄMEN
Christmas Oratorio (B.W. V², p. 124)

Hymn by Paul Gerhardt 1653　　　　　　　　　　　Melody by J.G. Ebeling 1666
Translation by Catherine Winkworth

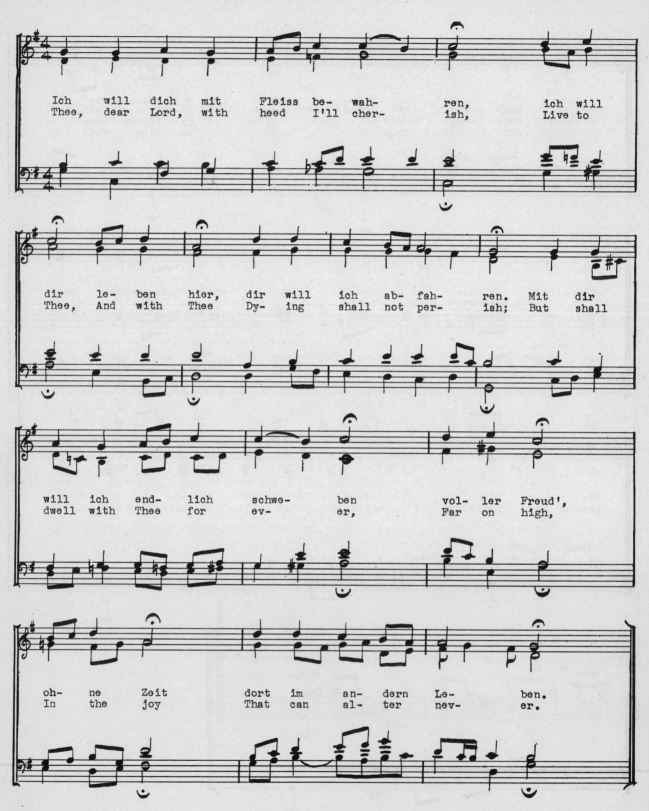

Ich　will　dich　mit　Fleiss be- wah- ren,　ich will
Thee,　dear　Lord,　with　heed I'll cher- ish,　Live to

dir　le- ben　hier,　dir　will　ich　ab- fah- ren.　Mit　dir
Thee,　And　with　Thee　Dy- ing　shall　not per- ish;　But　shall

will　ich　end- lich　schwe- ben　vol- ler　Freud',
dwell　with　Thee　for　ev- er,　Far　on　high,'

oh- ne　Zeit　dort　im　an- dern　Le- ben.
In　the　joy　That　can　al- ter　nev- er.

Cantata 69 Lobe den Herrn, meine Seele (B.W. XVI, p. 379)

Hymn by Samuel Rodigast 1675   Melody from Nürnbergisches Gesang-Buch 1690
Translation by Catherine Winkworth

Was   Gott   thut,   das   ist   wohl-   ge-than,   da-
Es   mag   mich   auf   die   rau-   he Bahn   Noth,
What-   e'er   my   God   or-   dains   is   right,   Here
Though   sor-   row,   need,   or   death   be   mine,   Yet

bei   will   ich   ver-   blei-   ben.   so   wird   Gott   mich   ganz
Tod   und   E-   lend   trei-   ben:
shall   my   stand be   ta-   ken;   My   Fa-   ther's care   Is
am   I   not for-   sa-   ken,

vä-   ter-   lich   in   sei-   nen Ar-   men   hal-   ten. Drum
around   me   there, He   holds   me   that   I   shall   not fall, And

lass   ich   ihn   nur   wal-   ten.
so   to   Him   I   leave it   all.

* Chord third appears in the instrumental accompaniment.

No.144   WAS MEIN GOTT WILL, DAS G'SCHEH' ALLZEIT

Cantata 144 Nimm, was dein ist. (B. W. XXX, p. 92)

Hymn by Albrecht, Markgraf of Brandenburg-Culmbach c. 1554
Translation by John S. Dwight

Melody of Secular song Il me suffit de
tous mes maulx c. 1530

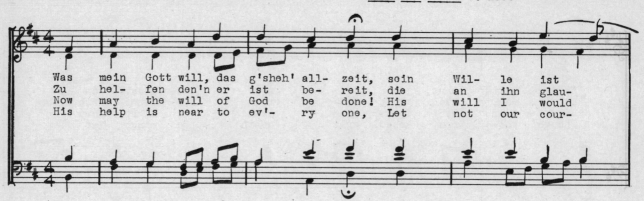

Was   mein   Gott will, das g'sheh' all-   zeit, sein   Wil   le   ist
Zu   hel-   fen den'n er ist   be-   reit, die   an   ihn   glau-
Now   may   the will of God   be   done! His   will   I   would
His   help   is   near to ev'-   ry   one, Let   not   our   cour-

- der   be-   ste.   Er   hilft   aus   Noth, -
- ben   fe-   ste.
- not   al-   ter.   In   all   our   need   -
- age   fal-   ter.

-   der   from- me Gott, und   züch- ti-   get   mit   Maa-
-, Our   Friend in- deed, How   ten-   der-   ly   He   chid-

168

ssen.   Wer   Gott   ver-traut,   fest   auf   ihn   baut,   den
eth!:   To   Him   hold   fast;   He   builds   to   last,   Who

will   er   nicht   —   ver-las-   sen.
still   in   God   —   con-fid-   eth..

No. 145   WAS MEIN GOTT WILL, DAS GESCHEH' ALLZEIT

St. Matthew Passion (B.W. IV, p. 83)

Hymn by Albrecht, Markgraf of Brandenburg-Culmbach c. 1554
Translation by John S. Dwight   Melody of secular song Il me suffit de
                                        tous mes maulx c. 1530

Was   mein   Gott   will, das   g'scheh' allzeit, sein   will'   der   ist der
Zu   hel-   fen   den'n er   ist   be-reit, die   an   ihn   glau-ben
Now   may   the   will of   God   be   done! His   will   I   would not
His   help   is   near to   ev'-   ry   one, Let   not   our   cour-age

be- ste; er hilft aus Noth, der from- me Gott, und
fe- ste;
al- ter. In all our need, Our Friend in- deed, How
fal- ter.

züch- ti- get mit Maa- ssen. Wer Gott ver- traut, fest
ten- der- ly He chid- eth!! To Him hold fast: He

auf ihn baut, den will er nicht ver- las- sen.
builds to last, Who will still in God con- fid- eth.

WELT, ADE! ICH BIN DEIN MÜDE

Cantata 27 Wer weiss, wie nahe mir mein Ende (B.W. v¹, p. 244)

Hymn by Johann Albinus 1649
Translation by Catherine Winkworth

Melody by Johann Rosenmüller 1649

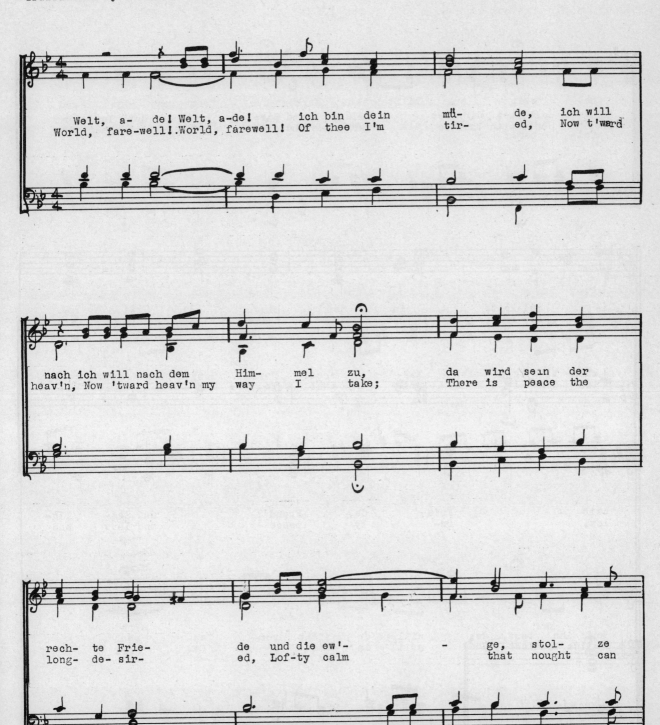

Ruh.   Welt, bei dir ist   Krieg   und Streit,   nichts, denn lau- ter
break: World with thee is   war   and strife,   Thou   with cheat-ing

Ei-   tel-keit;   in   dem   Him—   mel   al-   le-
hopes   are rife,   But   in   heav'n   is   no   al-

zeit   Frie-   de,   Freud'   und See—   lig-
loy,   On—   ly   peace   and love   and

keit.
joy.

WENN MEIN STÜNDLEIN VORHANDEN IST

(B.W. XXXIX, p. 270)

Hymn by Nicolaus Herman 1562   Melody from Württemberg Gross Kirchen Gesangbuch 1596
Translation by Catherine Winkworth

Wenn mein Stünd- lein vor- han- den ist und   ich soll fahr'n mein'
When my   last hour is   close at hand, And   I   must hence be-

Stra-   sse,   so   g'leit' du mich, Herr Je- su Christ, mit
take   me,   Do   Thou, Lord Je- sus, by   me stand, Nor

Hülf' mich nicht ver- las-   se: mein' Seel' an   mei- nem
let Thine aid for- sake   me; To   Thy blest hands I

letz- ten End' be- fehl' ich, Herr, in dei- ne Hand', du
now com- mend My soul, at this my earth- ly end, And

wirst sie wohl be- wah - - ren.
Thou wilt safe- ly keep it.

No. 148   WENN WIR IN HÖCHSTEN NÖTHEN SEIN

(B.W. XXXIX, p. 272)

Hymn by Paul Eber c. 1560   Melody by Louis Bourgeois 1547
Translation by Catherine Winkworth

Wenn   wir   in   höch- sten   Nö- - - - ten
When   in   the   hour of   ut- - - - most

sein   und   wis-   sen   nicht, wo   aus und ein, und
need   We   know not where to   look for aid, When

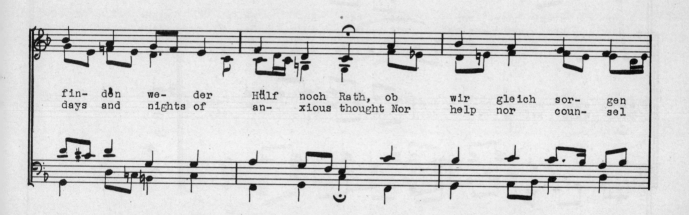

fin- den we- der   Hülf noch Rath, ob   wir gleich sor-   gen
days and nights of   an- xious thought Nor   help nor   coun- sel

früh und spat.
yet have brought.

Cantata 179 Siehe zu, dass deine Gottesfurcht nicht Heuchelei sei (B.W. XXXV, p. 292)

Hymn by Christoph Tietze c. 1663   Melody by Georg Neumark 1641
Translation Cento

WER NUR DEN LIEBEN GOTT LÄSST WALTEN

(B.W. XXXIX, p. 273)

Hymn by Georg Neumark 1641   Melody by Georg Neumark 1641
Translation by Catherine Winkworth

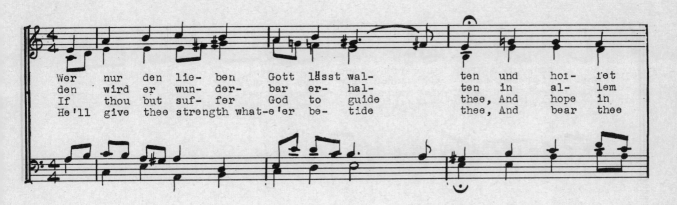

Wer nur den lie- ben Gott lässt wal-   ten und hoi- fet
den wird er wun- der- bar er- hal-   ten in al- lem
If thou but suf- fer God to guide   thee, And hope in
He'll give thee strength what-e'er be- tide   thee, And bear thee

auf ihn al- le- rig-   zeit,   Wer   Gott dem al- ler-
Kreuz und Trau- rig-   keit.   Who   trust in God's un-
Him through all thy   ways,
through the e- vil   days.

höch-   sten traut, der hat auf kei- nen   Sand ge- baut.
chang-   ing love Builds on the rock that   nought can move.

Cantata 197 Gott ist unser Zuversicht (B.W. XIII¹, p. 144)

* Hymn by Georg Neumark 1641   Melody by Georg Neumark 1641
  Translation by Catherine Winkworth

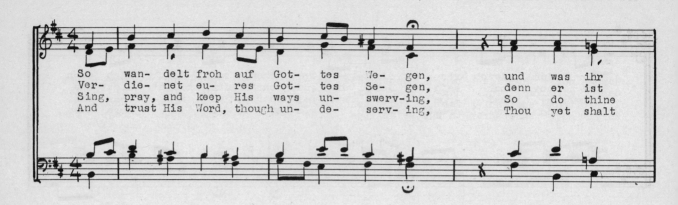

So   wan- delt froh auf Got-   tes We- gen,   und   was ihr
Ver- die- net eu- res Got- tes Se- gen,   denn er   ist
Sing, pray, and keep His ways un- swerv-ing,   So   do   thine
And   trust His Word, though un- de- serv- ing,   Thou yet shalt

thut, das thut ge-   treu!   denn wel- cher sei-   ne
al-   le   Mor- gen   neu: God   nev- er   yet   for-
own   part faith-ful- ly,
find   it   true for   thee;

Zu-   ver-sicht auf Gott setzt, den   ver-   lässt er   nicht.
sook   at need The soul that trust-ed   Him in-   deed.

* Bach's text differs from the original.

178

St. Matthew Passion (B.W. IV, p. 173)

Hymn by Johann Rist 1642
Translation by John S. Dwight

Melody by Johann Schop 1642

Bin ich gleich von dir ge-wi-chen, stell' ich mich doch
uns doch sein Sohn ver-gli-chen durch sein' Angst und
Though my feet from Thee have wan-der'd, Yet my heart was
on Thy great love I pon-der'd, Bear-ing more than

wie- der ein;　Hat
To- des-pein.
Thine a- gain　When
mor- tal pain.

Ich ver-leug- ne nicht die Schuld,
I the guilt do not dis- own;

a- ber dei- ne Gnad' und Huld ist viel grös- ser
But Thy par- d'ning grace a- lone Great- er is than

als die Sün- de, die ich stets in mir be- fin- de.
all the sin, That I al- ways feel with- in.

Cantata 172 Erschallet, ihr Lieder (B.W. XXXV, p. 69)

Hymn by Philipp Nicolai 1597   Melody adapted by Philipp Nicolai 1599
Translation by Catherine Winkworth

* Chord third appears in instrumental accompaniment.

Cantata 40 Dazu ist erschienen der Sohn Gottes (B.W. VII, p. 377)

Hymn by Caspar Fuger 1592
Translation by Catherine Winkworth

Melody from Dresden Gesangbuch 1593

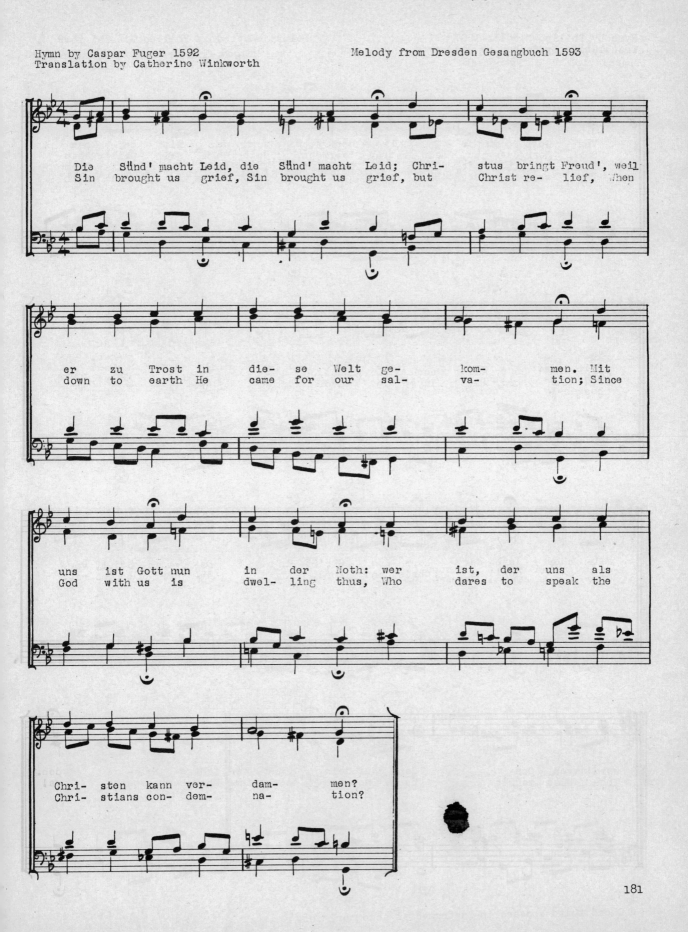

Die Sünd' macht Leid, die Sünd' macht Leid; Chri- stus bringt Freud', weil
Sin brought us grief, Sin brought us grief, but Christ re- lief, When

er zu Trost in die- se Welt ge- kom- men. Mit
down to earth He came for our sal- va- tion; Since

uns ist Gott nun in der Noth: wer ist, der uns als
God with us is dwel- ling thus, Who dares to speak the

Chri- sten kann ver- dam- men?
Chri- stians con- dem- na- tion?

Christmas Oratorio (B.W. V² p. 126)

Hymn by Christoph Runge 1653
Translation by J. Troutbeck

Melody from Dresden Gesangbuch 1593

Seid froh, die weil, seid froh, die weil dass eu- er Heil ist
Re- joice and sing! Re- joice and sing! Your gra- cious King. As

nie ein Gott und auch ein Mensch ge- bo- ren, der
man is born, and lays a- side His glo- ry; He

wel- cher ist der Herr und Christ in Da- vids Stadt, von
is a- dor'd As Christ and Lord, And ev- 'ry tongue re-

Vie- len aus- er- ko- ren.
peats the won- drous sto- ry.

182

Hymn by Martin Luther 1524   Melody from Klug's Geistliche Lieder 1535
Translation by Richard Massie

Wär' Gott nicht mit uns die se Zeit, so soll I- sra-el
wär' Gott nicht mit uns die se Zeit, wir hät- ten musst ver-
Had God not come, may Is- rael say, Had God not come to
Our en- e- mies on that sad day Would sure- ly have dis-

sa- gen: die so ein ar- mes Häuf- lein sind, ver-
za- gen, A rem- nant now, and hand- ful small, Held
aid us,
mayed us;

acht vor so viel Men- schen-kind, die an uns se- tzen
in con- tempt and scorn by all Who cru- el- ly op-

Al- le.
press us.

183

SWEDISH CHORALES
1-22

ALLENA GUD I HIMMELRIK   (24B)

(Allein Gott in der Höh sei Ehr)

Hymn adapted by Decius 1525
Translation by Catherine Winkworth

Melody from Schumann's Geistliche Lieder 1539

All glo- ry be to Thee, Most High, To

Thee all a- dor- a- tion! In

grace and truth Thou draw- est nigh To

of- fer us - sal- va - - tion. Thou

show- est Thy good will to men, And

peace shall reign on earth a- gain; We

praise Thy Name for- ev- er.

Hymn by F.M. Franzen c. 1814
Translation by P.M. Lindberg

Melody from Klug's Geistliche Lieder 1535

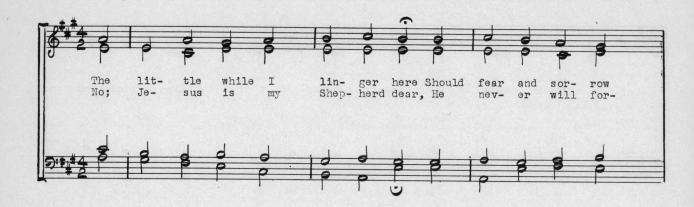

The lit- tle while I lin- ger here Should fear and sor- row
No; Je- sus is my Shep- herd dear, He nev- er will for-

fret me? He gave His life His flock to save, His
get me.

Spir- it and His Word He gave. With these He's ev- er with us.

No. 3   **DITT HUFVUD, JESU! BÖJES**   (91)

(O Haupt voll Blut und Wunden)

Hymn by Paul Gerhardt 1656   Melody by Melchior Teschner 1613
Translation by J.W. Alexander

O sa- cred head now wound- ed, With grief and

shame weighed down, Now scorn- ful- ly sur- round- ed,

With thorns Thine on- ly crown! Once reigning

in the high- est   In   light and   maj- es-   ty,   Dis-

hon- ored now Thou di- est,   Yet   here I   wor- ship Thee.

No. 4   EN DAG SKALL UPPGÅ FÖR VÅR SYN   (498)

Hymn by Bartholomäus Ringwaldt c. 1565   Melody from Koralbok 1697
Translation by P.A. Peter

The   day   is   sure- ly   draw- ing   near,   When
Will   with   great   maj- es-   ty ap-   pear,   As

188

He, the Lord's A- noint- ed,   No more the
Judge of all ap- point- ed.

gos- pel call is heard   To turn from sin and

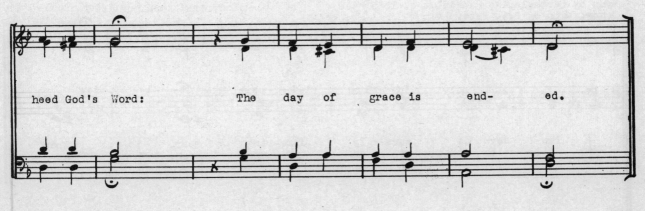

heed God's Word: The day of grace is end- ed.

189

(Puer natus in Bethlehem)

14th Century Latin hymn   Melody from Lossius' Psalmodia 1553
Translation anonymous

190

GUD HAR AF SIN BARMHERTIGHET (144)

(Es ist das Heil uns kommen her)

Hymn by Paul Speratus 1523
Translation by G.T. Rygh

Melody from Etlich Christlich Lyeder 1524

He that be- lieves and is bap- tized Shall
Bap- tized in- to the death of Christ, He

see the Lord's sal- va- a- tion; Through Christ's re-
is a new cre- a- tion;

demp-tion he shall stand A- mong the glo- rious

heaven-ly band Of ev- 'ry tribe and na- tion.

(Gott sei gelobet und gebenedeiet)

Hymn by Martin Luther 1524   Melody from Walter's Geistliche Gesangk Buchleyn 1524
Translation by Richard Massie

May   God   be   praised hence- forth and   blest for- ev- er!
With   His   own flesh and   blood our   souls doth nour- ish;

Who Him- self both   gift and   giv- er,   Oh,   Lord, have
May they   grow there- by and   flour-ish!

mer- cy   on   us.   By   Thy   ho- ly   bod- y, Lord, the

same   Which from   Thine own   moth- er   Ma-   ry

192

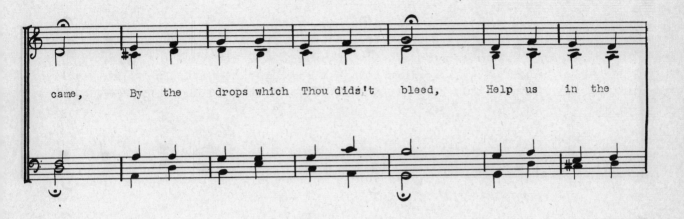

came, By the drops which Thou dids't bleed, Help us in the

hour of need. Oh Lord, have mer- cy on us.

No. 8   I HOPPET SIG MIN FRÄLSTA SJÄL FÖRNÖJER   (487)

Hymn by Elle Andersdatter c. 1645   Melody from 17th century
Translation by G.H. Trabert

In   hope   my   soul,   re- deemed   to   bliss   un- end- ing,
To   heav- en's   glo- rious   height   by   faith   as- cend- ing,

Is mind- ful ev- er That Christ did sev- er

The bonds of death, that I might live for- ev- er.

No. 9   KOM HELGE ANDE! HERRE GOD   (133)

Hymn by Martin Luther 1524   Melody from Walter's Geistliche gesangk Buchleyn 1524
Translation by C... Foss

Come, Ho- ly Spir- it, from a- bove, And

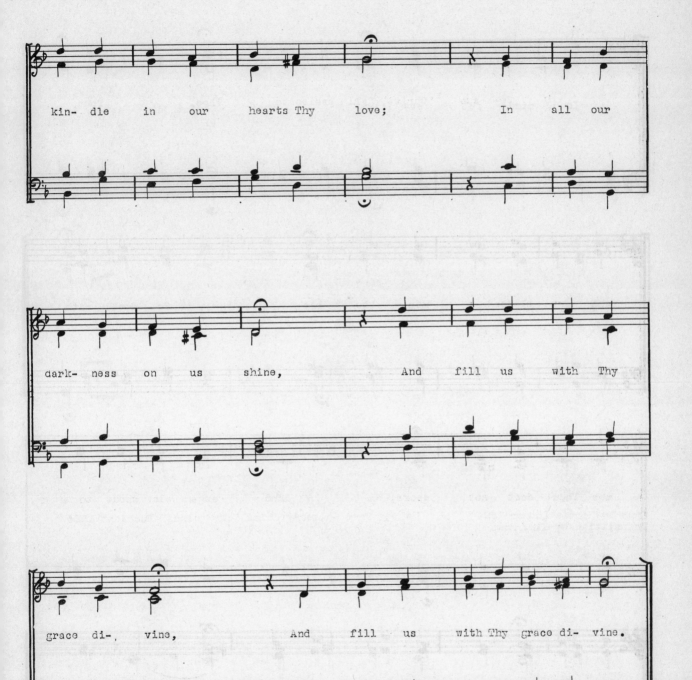

(Gelobet seist du Jesu Christ)

Hymn by Martin Luther 1524   Melody from Walter's Geistliche Gesangk Buchleyn 1524
Translation by A. T. Russell

O Je- sus Christ, all praise to Thee, Thou who art pleased a man to be; To dwell with men Thou dost not scorn, And ang- els shout to see Thee born, Hal- le- lu- jah.

Hymn by P. Hegelund 1586
Translation by O.T. Sanden

Melody c. 1542

De- spair not, O   heart, in thy   sor-   row, But

hope from God's prom-is- es   bor-   row;   Be-

ware, in thy   sor- row, of   sin-   ning,   For

death is of   life the be-   gin-   ning.

Hymn by Olaus Petri c. 1552   Melody from Strassburger Kirchenamt 1525
Translation by Augustus Nelson

Our   Fa- ther,   mer- ci-   ful and   good,   Who
Oh!   cleanse us   in   our   Sav- iour's blood,   And

dost   to   Thee in- vite   us,   Send   un- to
to   Thy- self u-   nite   us.

us Thy ho- ly   Word,   And   let   it   guide us

198

ev- er; Then in this world of dark- ness,

Lord, Shall naught from Thee us sev- er:

Grant us, O Lord, this fa- vor!

199

Hymn by J. Svedberg c. 1735
Translation anonymous

Melody from Koralbok 1697

'Tis fin- ished! So the Sav- iour cried, And

meek- ly bowed His head and died: 'Tis fin- ished!

yes, the race' is run, The bat- tle fought, the vict'ry won.

(Christ lag in Todesbanden)

Hymn by J. O. Wallin 1839   Melody from Walter's Geystliche Gesangk Buchleyn 1524
Translation by Felix Hanson

The eyes of Je-sus see a-gain, And dark-ness
Death seeks to hold that life in vain, That once for

now is driv-en. Je-sus from the tomb comes nigh
us was giv-en.

With Res-ur-rec-tion ban-nered high Pro-claim-ing

life e-ter-nal. Hal-le-lu-jah!

(In dulci jubilo)

Hymn by J.O. Wallin 1839
Translation by A.T. Russell

Melody from Klug's Geistliche Lieder 1535

Now sing we, now re-joice - -, Now raise to heaven our voice - -; Lo! He from whom joy stream- eth, Poor in the man- ger lies - -; Yet

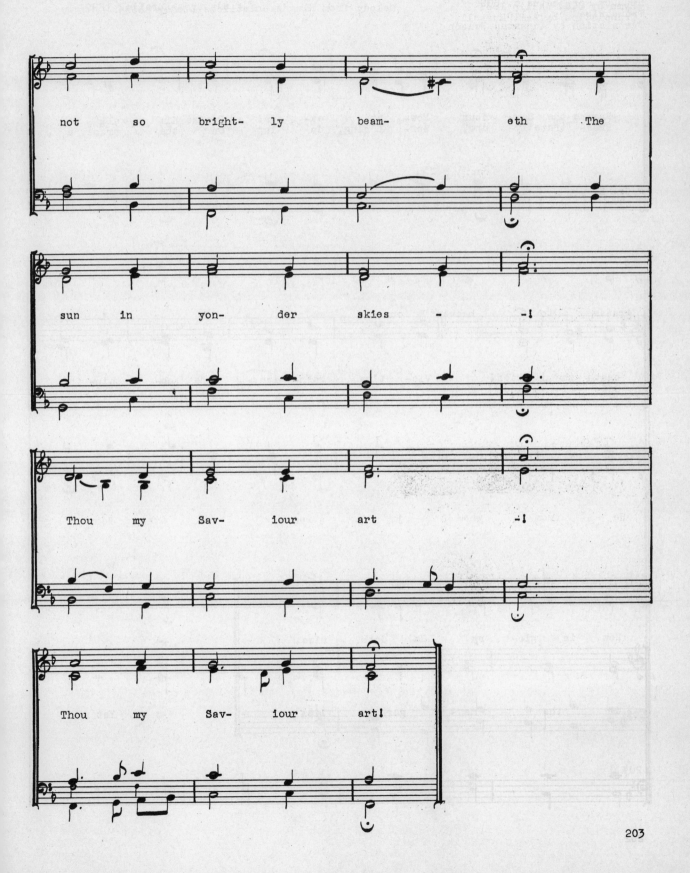

not so bright- ly beam- eth The

sun in yon- der skies - -!

Thou my Sav- iour art -!

Thou my Sav- iour art!

Hymn by Fortunatus c. 609
Transcribed by Wallin
Translation by Augustus Nelson

Melody from Koralbok 1697

Praise the Sav- iour   Now   and   ev- er!   Praise Him   all be-
Pros- trate ly- ing,   Suf- f'ring, dy- ing   On   the   cross, a

neath the   skies!   Vic- t'ry gain- ing,   Life ob-   tain- ing,
Sac- ri- fice;

Now   in glo- ry   He doth   rise.

204

(Wie schön leuchtet der Morgenstern)

Hymn by J.O. Wallin 1839
Translation by E.W. Olson

Melody adapted by Philipp Nicolai 1599

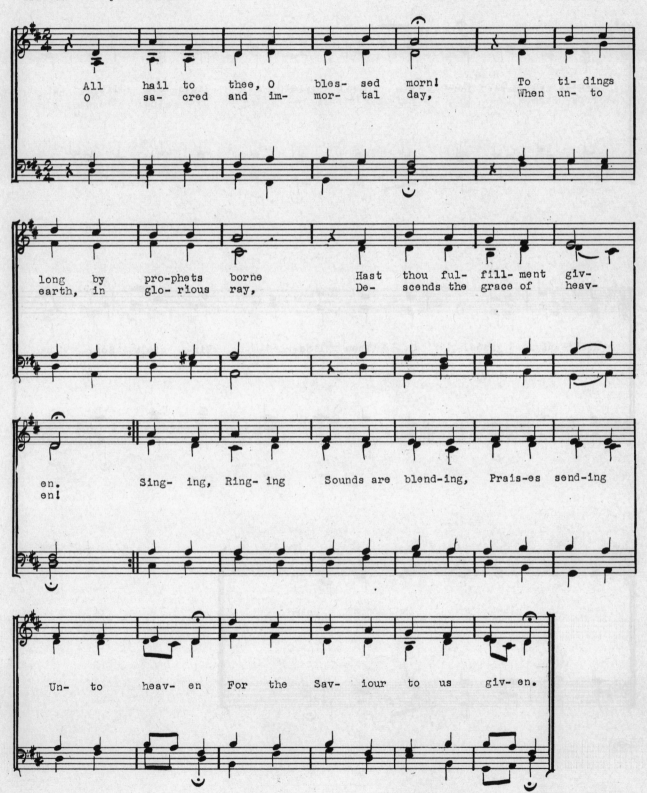

All hail to thee, O bles-sed morn! To ti-dings
O sa-cred and im-mor-tal day, When un-to

long by pro-phets borne Hast thou ful-fill-ment giv-
earth, in glo-rious ray, De-scends the grace of heav-

en.
en!

Sing-ing, Ring-ing Sounds are blend-ing, Prais-es send-ing

Un-to heav-en For the Sav-iour to us giv-en.

No. 18.   VERLDEN'S FRÄLSARE KOM HÄR   (58A)

(Nun komm der Heiden Heiland)

Hymn by Martin Luther 1524
Translation by W.H. Reynolds

Melody from Erfurter Enchiridion 1524

Come, Thou Sav- iour of our race, Choic- est Gift of

heav'- nly grace! O Thou bless- ed Vir- gin's Son,

Be Thy race on earth be- gun.

206

Hymn by J.O. Wallin 1816   Melody from Rostockerhandboken 1529
Translation Cento

Je- ho- vah, Thee we glo- ri- fy, Ru-

ler up- on Thy throne on high! O let Thy

Word Thro' all the earth be heard. Ho- ly, ho-

ly, ho- ly art Thou, O Lord.

(Ein' feste Burg ist unser Gott)

Hymn by Martin Luther 1527   Melody by Martin Luther 1527
Translation Cento

A   might- y   For- tress is   our   God,   A
He   helps us in   our ev- 'ry   need   That

trust- y Shield and   Weap -   on,   The - old ma-
hath us now o'er- tak -   en.

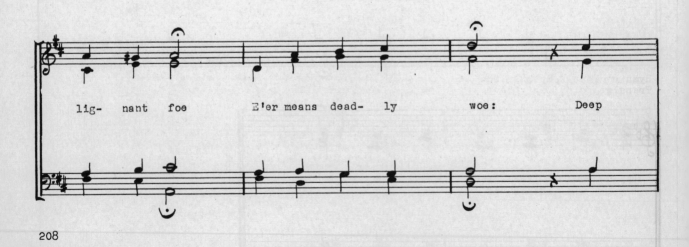

lig- nant foe   E'er means dead- ly   woe: Deep

guile and cru- el might　　Are　his　dread arms　in

fight,　　On　earth is　not his　e-　qual.

No. 21　　VÅR HERRAS JESU KRISTI DÖD　(154)

(Mein Seel, o Herr, muss loben dich)

Hymn by Haguin Spegel 1686　　　　　　Melody by Bartholomäus Gesius 1601
Translation by Olaf Olson

The　death of　Je- sus　Christ, our　Lord,　　We

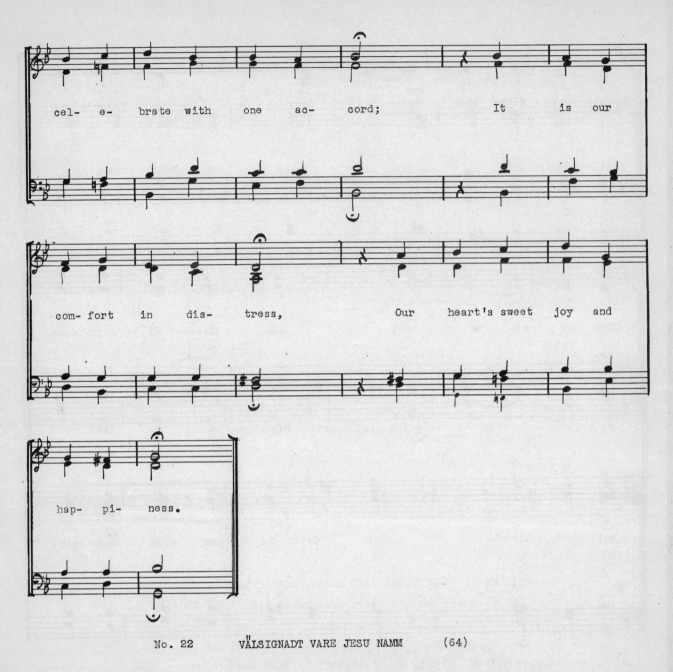

cel- e- brate with one ac- cord; It is our

com- fort in dis- tress, Our heart's sweet joy and

hap- pi- ness.

No. 22   VÄLSIGNADT VARE JESU NAMM   (64)

Hymn by J. Åström
Translation by Felix Hanson

Melody from Swedish Psalmbok 1567

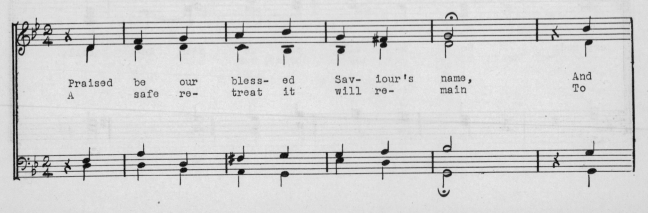

Praised   be   our   bless- ed   Sav- iour's   name,   And
A   safe   re- treat   it   will   re- main   To

praises with- out end— ing;
which our ways are wend— ing.

To heav'n a-

bove He will us call   His bless- ed chil- dren

well be- loved.   Our faith is now with tri- umph

crowned;   No e- vil can us e'er be- fall.

NORWEGIAN CHORALES
1-20

No. 1   AKK HERRE GUD (2b)

(Ach Gott und Herr)

Hymn by Johann Major 1613
Translation by Catherine Winkworth

Melody from As hymnodus sacer 1625

A- las! my God! My sins are great, My con-science doth up-

braid me; And now I find That at my strait No

man hath power to aid me.

212

No. 2   ALENE GUD I HIMMERIK (5)

(Allein Gott in der Höh sei Ehr)

Hymn adapted by Nicolaus Decius 1525   Melody from Schumann's Geistliche Lieder 1539
Translation by Catherine Winkworth

All glo-ry be to God on high, Who hath our race be-

friend- ed! To us no harm shall now come nigh, The

strife at last is end- ed; God show- eth His good

will t'ward men, And peace shall dwell on earth a- gain; O

thank   Him   for   His   good-   ness!

No. 3   **AV HÖIHETEN**   (12)

(Wie schön leuchtet der Morgenstern)

Hymn by Philipp Nicolai 1597   Melody adapted by Philipp Nicolai 1599
Translation by E.J. Palmer

The   Morn- ing   Star up-   on   us   gleams; How   full of   grace and

truth His   beams, How   pass- ing   fair   His   splen- dor!   Good

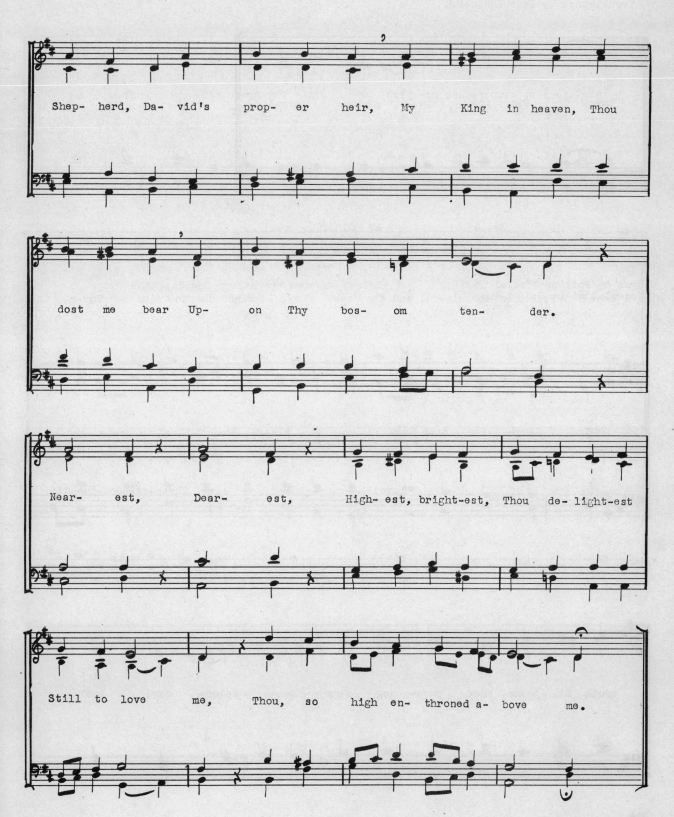

Shep- herd, Da- vid's prop- er heir, My King in heaven, Thou

dost me bear Up- on Thy bos- om ten- der.

Near- est, Dear- est, High- est, bright-est, Thou de- light-est

Still to love me, Thou, so high en- throned a- bove me.

No. 4   BRYT FREM, MITT HJERTES TRANG AT LINDRE (14A)

Hymn by L.A. Gotler 1714
Translation by Jane Borthwick

Melody by L.M. Lindeman c. 1871

Sav- iour of sinners now re- vive us   With Thy free mer- cy   from a-

bove;   Friend of the sin-ful and the wea- ry,   Turn un- to   us   Thy

heart   of   love!   O   come, Thy sweet com-pas-sion

show- ing,   On   our poor souls Thy grace be- stow- ing.

(Christ lag in Todesbanden)

Hymn by Martin Luther 1524   Melody from Walter's Geystliche Gesangk Buchleyn 1524
Translation by Richard Massie

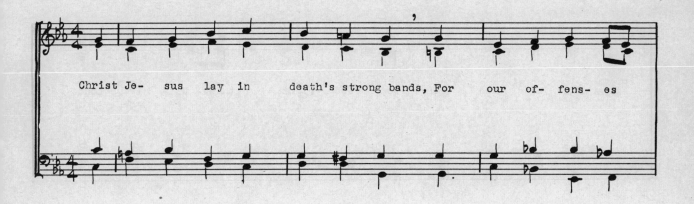

Christ Je- sus lay in   death's strong bands, For   our   of- fens- es

giv-   en; But   now   at God's   right   hand   He   stands, And

brings us   life   from   heav-   en: Where- fore let   us

217

joy- ful be And sing to God right thank- ful- ly Loud

songs of Hal- le- lu- jah! Hal- le- lu- jah!

No. 6   DET HEV EI ROSA SPRUNGE (26)

(Es ist ein Ros entsprungen)

15th or 16th Century Twelfth Night Carol   Melody from Kölnischer Gesangbuch 1599
Translation anonymous

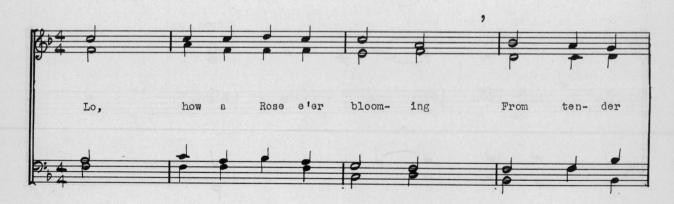

Lo,   how a Rose e'er bloom- ing   From ten- der

stem hath sprung! Of Jes- se's lin- eage com- ing

As men of old have sung. It came, a flow'r-et

bright, A- mid the cold of win- ter,

When half spent was the night.

No. 7 DU VAERE LOVET, JESUS KRIST (36)

(Gelobet seist du Jesu Christ)

Hymn by Martin Luther 1524   Melody from Walter's Geistliche gesangk Buchleyn 1524
Translation by A.T. Russell

O Je- sus Christ, all praise to Thee, Thou who art pleased a

man to be; To dwell with men Thou dost not scorn, And

ang- els shout to see Thee born, Hal- le- lu-   ja.

(Puer natus in Bethlehem)

14th Century Latin hymn
Translation by Philip Schaff

Melody from Lossius' Psalmodia 1553

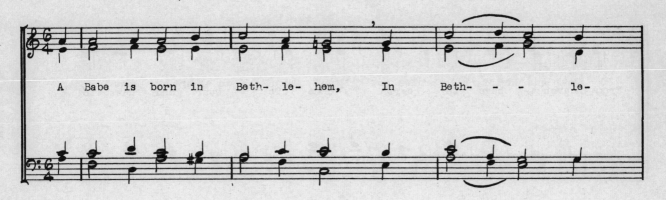

A Babe is born in Beth- le- hem, In Beth- - - le-

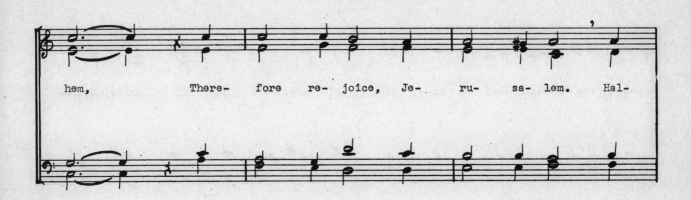

hem,   There- fore re- joice, Je- ru- sa- lem. Hal-

le- lu- ja, hal- le- - - lu- ja!

(Vom Himmel hoch)

Hymn by Martin Luther 1535   Melody from Schumann's Geistliche Lieder 1539
Translation by Catherine Winkworth

From heaven a- bove to earth I come To bear good news to

ev- ery home; Glad ti- dings of great joy I bring, Where-

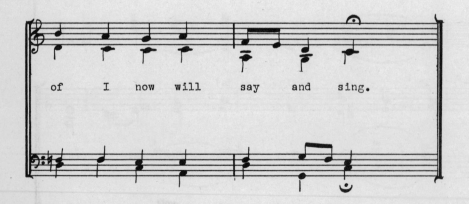

of I now will say and sing.

(Herr ich habe misgehandelt)

Hymn by Johann Franck 1649   Melody by Johann Crüger 1649
Translation by Catherine Winkworth

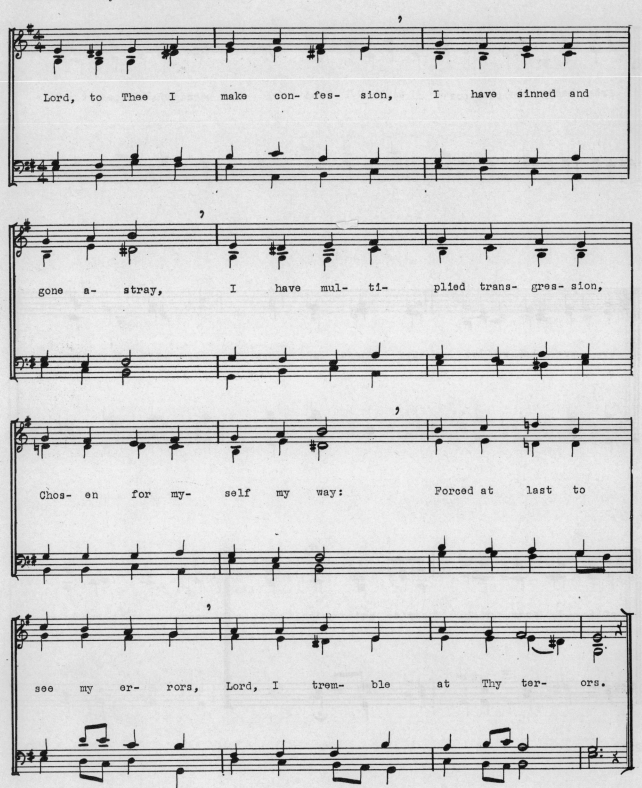

Lord, to Thee I make con- fes- sion, I have sinned and gone a- stray, I have mul- ti- plied trans- gres- sion, Chos- en for my- self my way: Forced at last to see my er- rors, Lord, I trem- ble at Thy ter- ors.

(Wer nur den lieben Gott lässt walten)

Hymn by Georg Neumark 1641
Translation by Catherine Winkworth

Melody by Georg Neumark 1641

If Thou but suf-fer God to guide thee, And

hope in Him through all thy ways, He'll give thee

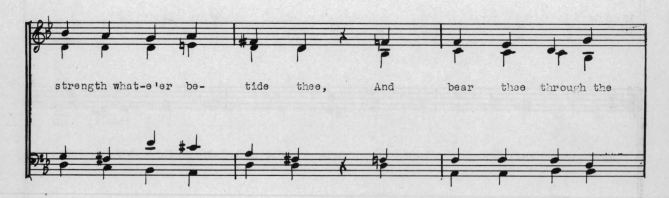

strength what-e'er be- tide thee, And bear thee through the

e- vil days;　　　Who trusts in　God's un- chang- ing

love　　Builds　on　the　rock　that　naught can　move.

No. 12　　　**JEG SYNGER JULEKVAD**　　　(119)

(In dulci jubilo)

15th Century Latin Hymn　　　　Melody from Klug's Geistliche Lieder 1535
Translation by A.T. Russell

Now　sing we, now re- joice,　　　Now　raise　to heaven　our

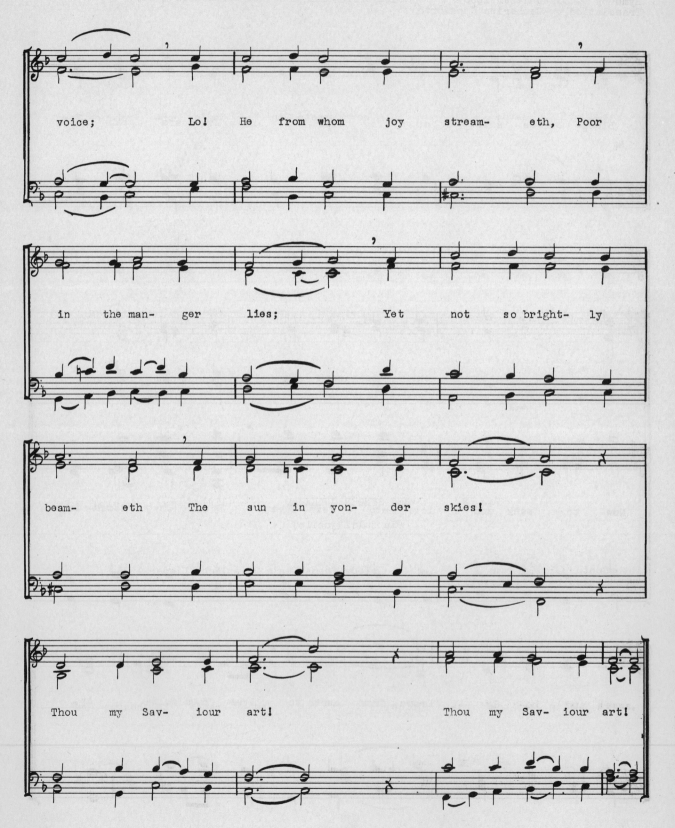

voice; Lo! He from whom joy stream- eth, Poor

in the man- ger lies; Yet not so bright- ly

beam- eth The sun in yon- der skies!

Thou my Sav- iour art! Thou my Sav- iour art!

JESUS, FRELSER, VI ER HER   (127A)

(Liebster Jesu wir sind hier)

Hymn by T. Clausnitzer 1663   Melody from Ahle's Sonntagsandachten 1664
Translation by Catherine Winkworth

Bless- ed Je- sus,   at Thy word   We are gath- ered
all to hear Thee; Let our hearts and souls be stirred
Now to seek and love and fear Thee; By Thy teach- ings
sweet and ho- ly Drawn from earth to love Thee sole- ly.

Hymn by N.F.S. Grundtvig 1837
Translation by C. Doving

Melody by L.H. Lindeman 1840

Built on the Rock the Church doth stand,

E- ven when stee- ples are fall- ing;

Crumb- led have spires in ev- ery land.

Bells still are chim- ing and call- ing;

Lull- ing the young and old to rest,

But a- bove all the soul dis- trest,

Long- ing for rest ev- er- last- ing.

(Komm, Gott Schöpfer, heiliger Geist)

Hymn by Martin Luther 1524   Melody from Klug's Geistliche Lieder 1535
Translation by Richard Massie

Come, Ho- ly Spir-it, God and Lord! Be   all Thy gra- ces

now   out- poured On   each be- liev- er's soul   and   heart; Thy

fer- vent love to   them im- part.

230

No. 16   **LOVER DEN HERRE**   (152)

(Lobe den Herren)

Hymn by J. Neander 1680   Melody from Stralsund Gesangbuch 1665
Translation by Catherine Winkworth

Praise to the Lord, the Al- might- y, the King of cre-

a- tion! O my soul, praise Him, for

He is thy health and sal- va- tion!

All ye who hear, How to His tem- ple draw

near, Join me in glad a- do- ra- tion.

No. 17   MIN SJEL OG ÅND, OPMUNTRE DIG   (165B)

Hymn by J.N. Bruń 1786
Translation by O.H. Smeby

Melody from Thomissöns Psalmebog 1569

How blest are they who hear God's word, And keep and heed what

they have heard: They wis- dom dai- ly gath- er; Their

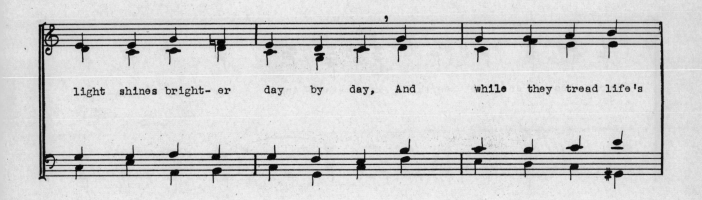

light shines bright-er day by day, And while they tread life's

wea- ry way, They have the oil of glad- ness To

soothe their pain and sad- ness.

233

Hymn by M.B. Landstad 1855
Translation by O.T. Sanden

Melody is a Sequence from the ancient Olavs-fest in Nidaros

Dark- ness o'er the earth is steal- ing In my lone- ly cham- ber kneel- ing, I will say my even- ing prayer, Long- ing for a clos- er un- ion, With my God I hold com- mun- ion And com- mit me to His care.

(Herzlich thut mich verlangen)

Hymn by Paul Gerhardt 1656   Melody by Hans Leo Hassler 1601
Translation by J.W. Alexander

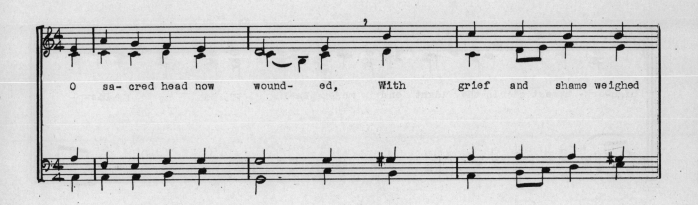

O sa- cred head now wound- ed, With grief and shame weighed

down,   Now   scorn- ful- ly   sur-   round- ed, With

thorns Thine on- ly   crown!   Once   reign- ing   in   the

235

high- est In light and maj- es- ty, Dis-

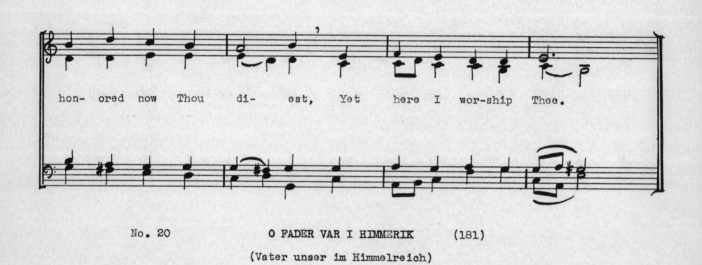

hon- ored now Thou di- est, Yet here I wor-ship Thee.

No. 20   **O FADER VAR I HIMMERIK**   (181)

(Vater unser im Himmelreich)

Hymn by Martin Luther 1539   Melody from Schumann's Geistliche Lieder 1539
Translation by Catherine Winkworth

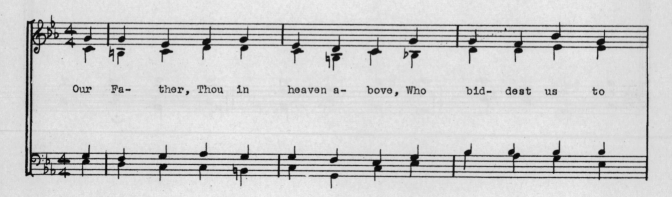

Our Fa- ther, Thou in heaven a- bove, Who bid- dest us to

236

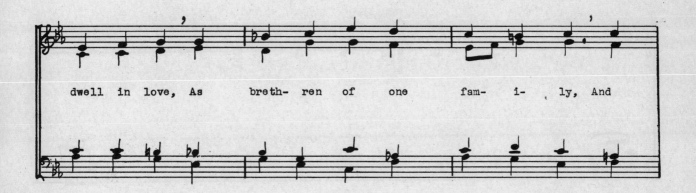

dwell in love, As breth- ren of one fam- i- ly, And

cry for all we need to Thee; Teach us to mean the

words we say, And from the in- most heart we pray.

237

tape Sew